GCSE

Biology

There are only three ways to make sure you're fully prepared for the Grade 9-1 AQA Foundation Level GCSE Biology exams — practice, practice and ~~knitting~~ practice.

That's why we've packed this brilliant CGP book with realistic exam-style questions on every topic. All the required practicals are covered too and there are plenty of targeted analysis questions to test those tricky AO3 skills.

There's even a section of mixed questions which test different topics, just like in the real exams. So what are you waiting for? Hurry up and get stuck in!

Exam Practice Workbook

Foundation Level

Contents

Use the tick boxes to check off the topics you've completed.

Topic 7 — Ecology

Mixed Questions

You can find some useful information about What to Expect in the Exams and other exam tips at cgpbooks.co.uk/GCSEBiologyFoundation/Exams

Published by CGP

Editors:
Luke Bennett, Eleanor Crabtree, Mary Falkner, Chris Lindle, Sarah Pattison, Rachael Rogers, Camilla Sheridan.

Contributors:
Sophie Anderson, Bethan Parry, Alison Popperwell.

With thanks to Susan Alexander and Glenn Rogers for the proofreading.

With thanks to Lottie Edwards for the copyright research.

Data in Figure 1 on page 31 source: Health Survey for England 2018. Licensed under the Open Government Licence v3.0 http://www.nationalarchives.gov.uk/doc/open-government-licence/version/3/

Data in Figure 2 on page 31 contains information from NHS Digital. Licensed under the Open Government Licence v3.0 http://www.nationalarchives.gov.uk/doc/open-government-licence/version/3/

ISBN: 978 1 78908 326 2

Clipart from Corel®
Printed by Elanders Ltd, Newcastle upon Tyne

Based on the classic CGP style created by Richard Parsons.

How to Use This Book

- Hold the book upright, approximately 50 cm from your face, ensuring that the text looks like this, not siɥʇ.
- Before attempting to use this book, read the following safety information:

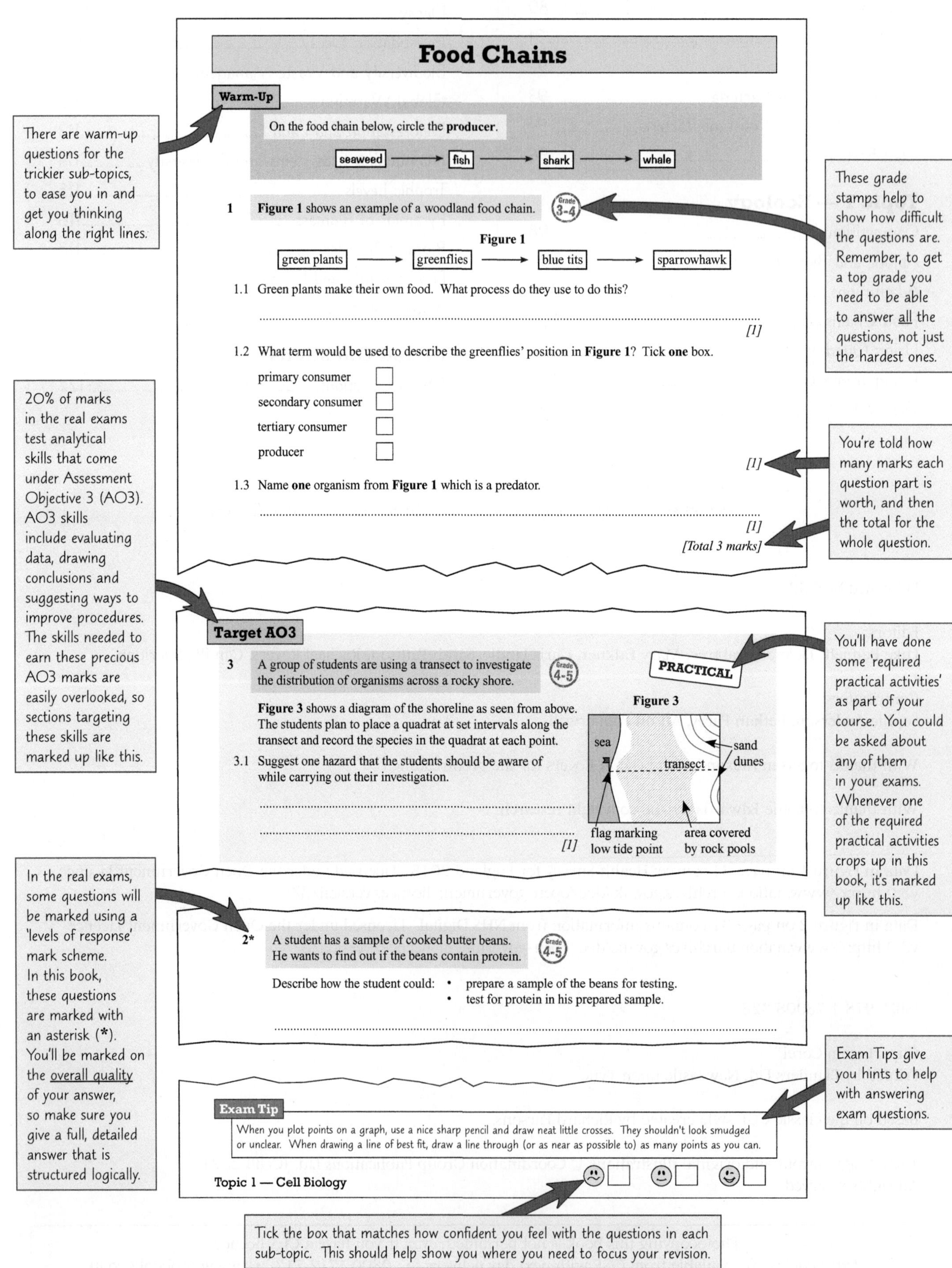

Cells

Warm-Up

Complete the table to show whether each statement is **true** for eukaryotic cells or prokaryotic cells. Tick **one** box in each row.

Statement	Eukaryotic cells	Prokaryotic cells
These cells have a nucleus.		
These are the smallest type of cell.		
These cells can be bacteria.		

1 **Figure 1** shows a diagram of an animal cell. 

Figure 1

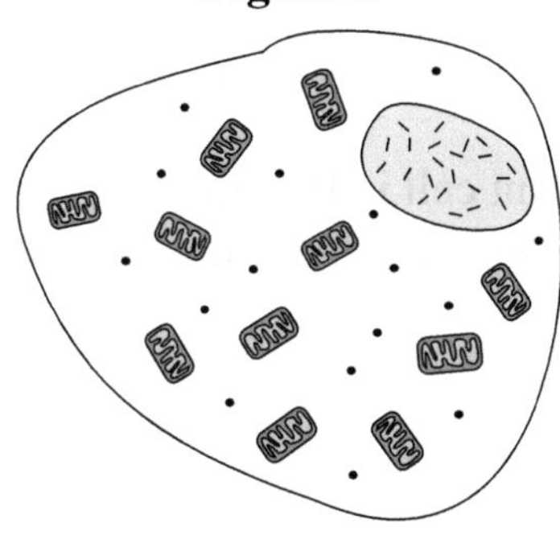

1.1 Label the cell membrane, the nucleus and a mitochondrion on **Figure 1**.

[3]

1.2 Give the function of each part of the cell on **Figure 1**.

Cell membrane ....

Mitochondria ....

Nucleus ....

[3]

1.3 Name **two** other subcellular structures that can be found in an animal cell.

1. ....

2. ....

[2]

1.4 Give **one** reason why the diagram in **Figure 1** does not represent a plant cell.

....

[1]

[Total 9 marks]

Exam Tip

If you get a question in the exam where you need to label a diagram, make sure you draw your label lines very carefully. If it's not clear what part of the diagram the end of your line is touching, you might miss out on some valuable marks.

Microscopy

1 A student observed blood cells under a microscope. A scale drawing of one of the cells is shown in **Figure 1**. Grade 1-3

Figure 1

A

In **Figure 1**, A is the image width.

1.1 Measure the length of A with a ruler. .... mm

[1]

1.2 The real width of the cell is 0.012 mm.
What is the magnification of the image in **Figure 1**?
Use the formula:

$$\text{magnification} = \frac{\text{image size}}{\text{real size}}$$

magnification = × ....

[1]

[Total 2 marks]

2 A plant cell is magnified 1000 times using a light microscope. Grade 3-4

2.1 The length of the image of the plant cell is 10 mm.
Calculate the real length of one plant cell in millimetres (mm).
Use the formula:

$$\text{real size} = \frac{\text{image size}}{\text{magnification}}$$

.... mm

[1]

2.2 What is the length of one plant cell in micrometres (μm)?

.... μm

[1]

2.3 How do magnification and resolution compare between electron and light microscopes?
Tick **one** box.

Magnification and resolution are the same for electron microscopes and light microscopes. ☐

Electron microscopes have a lower magnification and resolution than light microscopes. ☐

Electron microscopes have a higher magnification and resolution than light microscopes. ☐

[1]

2.4 Give **one** way in which electron microscopy has increased understanding of subcellular structures.

....

[1]

[Total 4 marks]

Exam Tip

Make sure that you know how to convert one unit to another. Remember, to go from a bigger unit to a smaller unit (for example, going from millimetres to micrometres) your calculation should be a multiplication. To go from a smaller unit to a bigger unit (for example, going from micrometres to millimetres) your calculation should be a division.

More on Microscopy

PRACTICAL

1 A student wants to use a light microscope to view a sample of onion cells. Grade 4-5

1.1 The student adds a drop of iodine stain to her sample. Which statement best describes why a stain might be used to view a sample of tissue? Tick **one** box.

To make the specimen easier to cut. ☐

To make the specimen easier to see. ☐

To prevent air bubbles forming. ☐

To help the cover slip stick to the slide. ☐

[1]

Figure 1 shows a diagram of the light microscope that the student plans to use.

1.2 The three different objective lenses are labelled in **Figure 1** with their magnification.

Which lens should the student select first when viewing her cells?

....

[1]

Figure 1

1.3 After she has selected the objective lens, she looks down the eyepiece and uses the adjustment knobs.

Describe the purpose of the adjustment knobs.

....

....

....

[1]

1.4 The student wants to see the cells at a greater magnification.

Describe the steps that she should take.

....

....

....

[2]

1.5 After she has viewed the cells, she wants to produce a scientific drawing of them. Her teacher has told her to use smooth lines to draw the structures she can see.

Give **two** other ways in which she can make sure she produces an accurate and useful drawing.

1. ....

2. ....

[2]

[Total 7 marks]

Exam Tip

The number of marks that a question is worth is sometimes a bit like a secret tip from the examiners about how much they want you to write. E.g. if a 'describe' question is worth two marks, you'll usually need to make two separate points.

Cell Differentiation and Specialisation

Warm-Up

Complete the sentence below. Use a word from the box.

specialisation	differentiation	adaptation

The process by which cells change to carry out specific functions is called ....

1 Specialised cells have different structures.
This allows them to carry out different functions. Grade 1-3

Draw straight lines to match up each type of plant cell with its structure and function.

Plant cell	Structure and Function
root hair cell	Long cells joined end to end, with very few subcellular structures. They transport food.
xylem	Long hollow cells joined end to end. They transport water.
phloem	Long, hair-like shape. They absorb water and mineral ions.

[Total 2 marks]

2 A sperm cell is specialised for its function. Grade 3-4

2.1 What is the function of a sperm cell?

....

[1]

Figure 1 shows a sperm cell.

Figure 1

tail

mitochondria

2.2 How does the sperm cell's **tail** help it to carry out its function?

....

[1]

2.3 Describe how **mitochondria** help the sperm cell to carry out its function.

....

[1]

[Total 3 marks]

Chromosomes and Mitosis

1 **Figure 1** shows a cell during the cell cycle. 

Figure 1

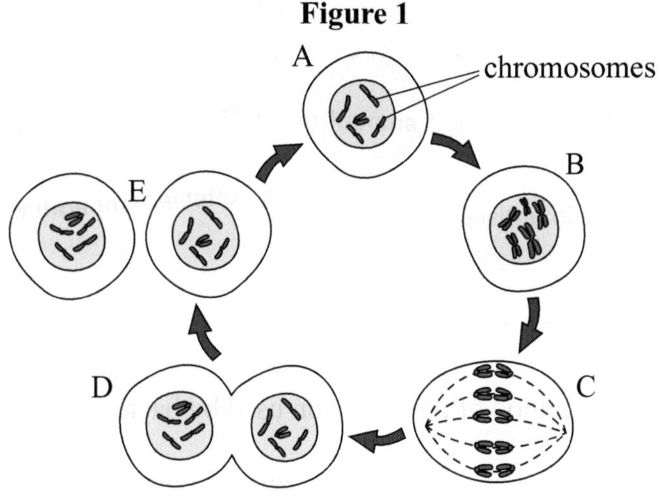

1.1 Cell **A** is preparing to divide. What is happening to the chromosomes in cell A?
Tick **one** box.

The chromosomes are dividing. ☐

The chromosomes are being copied. ☐

The chromosomes are getting longer. ☐

[1]

1.2 What else is happening in cell **A**?
Tick **one** box.

The number of mitochondria is increasing. ☐

The number of ribosomes is decreasing. ☐

The nucleus is dividing. ☐

[1]

1.3 Describe what is happening to cell **D**.

....

....

[2]

1.4 How do the two cells produced at stage **E** compare to cell **A**?
Tick **one** box.

They are genetically different. ☐

They are genetically similar. ☐

They are genetically identical. ☐

[1]

[Total 5 marks]

Exam Tip

In the exam, you might be given photos of real cells undergoing mitosis and asked what's going on. Don't panic if the cells themselves don't look familiar — the main thing you have to look at is what the chromosomes are doing.

Binary Fission

Warm-Up

Which of these conditions would help bacteria to divide quickly on an agar plate? Circle all of the correct answers.

sterilising the agar plate the right amount of nutrients plenty of light

discs soaked in antiseptics a suitable temperature

1 Bacteria reproduce using a type of simple cell division. Grade 1-3

1.1 What name is given to the method of reproduction used by bacteria?

....

[1]

1.2 The statements below describe the steps in the reproduction of bacteria. They are not in the correct order.

A Two new bacterial cells are produced. Each has one copy of the circular DNA.

B The cytoplasm of the bacterial cell divides and new cell walls form.

C The circular DNA inside a bacterial cell is copied.

What is the correct order for the statements above? Tick **one** box.

A, B, C ☐ B, C, A ☐ C, B, A ☐ B, A, C ☐

[1]

[Total 2 marks]

2 A type of bacteria has a mean division time of 45 minutes at 20 °C. One of these bacteria was left to reproduce for 9 hours at 20 °C. Grade 4-5

Calculate how many bacteria will be in the population after 9 hours. Complete the steps below.

Give 9 hours in minutes.

.... minutes

[1]

Work out how many divisions take place.

.... divisions

[1]

Work out the number of bacteria produced by this number of divisions.

.... bacteria

[1]

[Total 3 marks]

Culturing Microorganisms

PRACTICAL

1 A student investigated the effect of four different concentrations of an antiseptic on bacterial growth.

The four different concentrations (A-D) are shown in **Table 1**.

Table 1

Solution	A	B	C	D
Concentration	100%	50%	25%	12.5%

The student used agar plates that had bacteria spread evenly over the agar jelly.
She set up three plates in total. Each plate contained paper discs soaked in each of the solutions.
She set up the plates for her investigation using the following method:

1. Soak a paper disc in solution A and place it on one of the agar plates.
2. Repeat this with solutions B, C and D. Place the discs on the same agar plate.
3. Prepare two more plates in the same way. These two plates will be used for repeats.
4. Incubate the three plates at 25 °C for two days.

1.1 Why is it important that the plates were not incubated above 25 °C?

....

[1]

1.2 The student had to make sure that her plates did not become contaminated.
Which of the following statements is **false**? Tick **one** box.

The Petri dishes should have been sterilised before use. ☐

The student should tape the lids on the Petri dishes before incubating them. ☐

The student should store the plates with the lids at the top. ☐

Contamination could result in the growth of unwanted microorganisms, which could affect the results. ☐

[1]

After two days, the student measured the diameters of the inhibition zones around the discs.
The results for **solution B** are shown in **Table 2**.

Table 2

Diameter (mm)			
Plate 1	Plate 2	Plate 3	Mean
10	15	14	**X**

1.3 Calculate the value of **X** in **Table 2**.

.... mm

[1]

The student repeated the experiment using a different antiseptic.
Some of her results for this experiment are shown in **Table 3**.

Table 3

Concentration of solution	100%	50%	25%	12.5%
Mean radius of inhibition zone (mm)	11	8	5	4
Area of inhibition zone (cm^2)	3.8	2.0	**Y**	0.5

1.4 Calculate the value of **Y** to complete **Table 3**. Complete the steps below.
Give the mean radius in cm.

.... cm

Work out the area of the inhibition zone in cm^2. Use the formula πr^2, where $\pi = 3.14$.

.... cm^2

[2]

1.5 Complete **Figure 1**. Use **Table 3** to plot a graph of the area of the inhibition zone against the concentration of the solution for the 100%, 50% and 12.5% solutions.
Draw a line of best fit between the points.

Figure 1

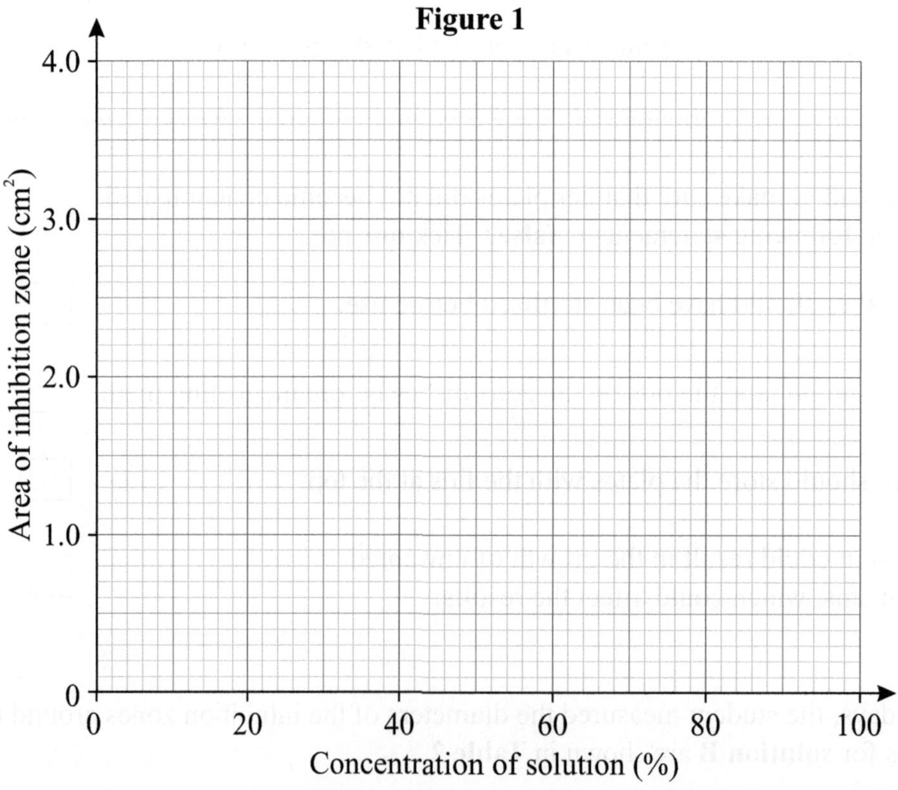

[2]

1.6 What type of correlation is shown between the concentration of the solution and the area of the inhibition zone?

....

[1]

[Total 8 marks]

Exam Tip

When you plot points on a graph, use a nice sharp pencil and draw neat little crosses. They shouldn't look smudged or unclear. When drawing a line of best fit, draw a line through (or as near as possible to) as many points as you can.

Stem Cells

1 Stem cells can be found in the growing areas of plants. (Grade 4-5)

1.1 What is a stem cell?

.... *[1]*

1.2 What are the growing areas of a plant that contain stem cells called?
Tick **one** box.

cloning zones ☐ meristems ☐ leaves ☐ mesophyll layers ☐

[1]

1.3 You can produce cloned plants from plant stem cells.
Describe **two** benefits of producing cloned plants from stem cells.

1. ....

2. .... *[2]*

[Total 4 marks]

2 The technique shown in **Figure 1** could be used to produce cells for some medical treatments. (Grade 4-5)

Figure 1

1. Stem cells extracted from bone marrow. → 2. Stem cells cloned. → nerve cells / insulin-producing cells

3. Different cell types are produced.

2.1 Name **one** medical condition that may be helped by treatment using stem cells.

.... *[1]*

2.2 Apart from bone marrow, give **one** other source of stem cells for medical treatments.

.... *[1]*

2.3 Suggest **one** reason why some people may be **against** using the source of stem cells you named in **2.2**.

.... *[1]*

2.4 Give **one** potential **risk** of using stem cells in medical treatments.

.... *[1]*

[Total 4 marks]

Exam Tip

You might be asked to write about the social or ethical issues to do with using stem cells. It's a good idea to know some different points of view, so that you have plenty to write about. You don't have to agree with the opinions.

 ☐  ☐  ☐

Diffusion

1 **Figure 1** shows glucose molecules diffusing through a cell membrane. 

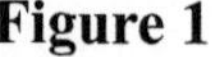

Figure 1

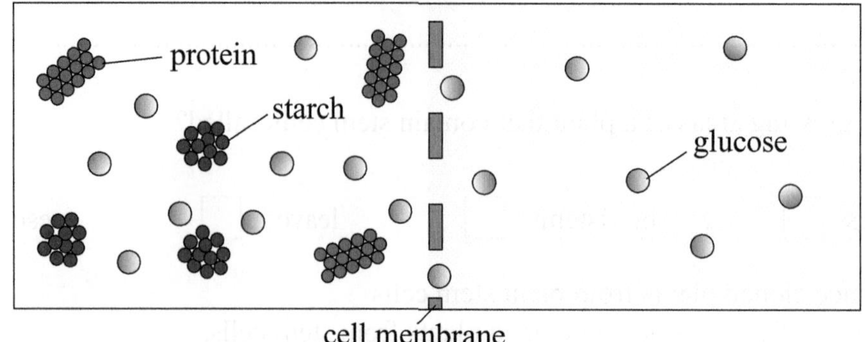

1.1 In which direction will most of the glucose molecules be moving?
Draw an arrow on **Figure 1** to show your answer.

[1]

1.2 Why can't the protein molecules in **Figure 1** diffuse through the membrane?

....

[1]

1.3 As glucose diffuses from one side of the membrane to the other, its concentration gradient decreases. Which statement is correct?
Tick **one** box.

A decrease in the concentration gradient will have no effect on the rate of diffusion. ☐

A decrease in the concentration gradient will increase the rate of diffusion. ☐

A decrease in the concentration gradient will decrease the rate of diffusion. ☐

[1]

[Total 3 marks]

2 A student adds a drop of ink to a glass of cold water. (Grade 4-5)

2.1 What will the student observe happening to the drop of ink?
Explain your answer.

....

....

....

[2]

2.2 How might the observation differ if the ink was added to a glass of warm water?

....

[1]

[Total 3 marks]

Exam Tip

Diagrams showing molecules diffusing through a cell membrane often crop up in the exams. Look at the labels on these sorts of diagrams carefully to check that you're answering about the type of molecule that you're being asked about.

Osmosis

1 Some molecules move by osmosis. 

1.1 Use the words in the box to complete the following definition of osmosis:

water	**more**	**less**	**sugar**

Osmosis is the movement of .... molecules across a partially permeable membrane from a .... concentrated solution to a .... concentrated solution.

[3]

1.2 In which of these is osmosis occurring? Tick **one** box.

A plant is absorbing water from the soil. ☐

Sugar is being taken up into the blood from the gut. ☐

Water is evaporating from a leaf. ☐

Oxygen is entering the blood from the lungs. ☐

[1]

[Total 4 marks]

PRACTICAL

2 A student did an experiment to see the effect of different salt solutions on pieces of potato. 

- He cut five equal-sized chips from a raw potato and measured the mass of each chip.
- Each chip was placed in a beaker containing a different concentration of salt solution.
- The mass of each chip was measured again after 24 hours. The results are shown in **Table 1**.

Table 1

Beaker	1	2	3	4	5
Mass of potato chip at start of experiment (g)	5.70	5.73	5.71	5.75	5.77
Mass of potato chip after 24 hours (g)	6.71	6.58	6.27	5.46	4.63
Percentage change in mass of potato chip (%)	17.7	?	9.81	–5.04	–19.8

2.1 Calculate the percentage change in mass for the potato chip in beaker 2.

.... %

[2]

2.2 Explain why the chips in beakers 4 and 5 lost mass.

....

....

[2]

[Total 4 marks]

Target AO3

3 A student is investigating osmosis. She takes two beakers and puts a different concentration of sucrose solution into each one. Then she places a length of Visking tubing (a partially permeable membrane) containing 0.5 M sucrose solution into each beaker. She places a glass capillary tube in the Visking tubing so that the end dips into the sucrose solution. A diagram of her experiment is shown in **Figure 1**.

Figure 1

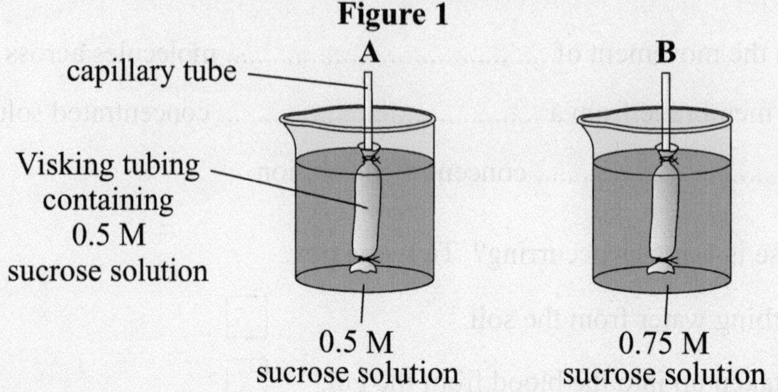

The student records the level of the sucrose solution in each beaker and each capillary tube at the start of the experiment. She plans to record the level of the solution in each beaker every 30 minutes for 8 hours.

3.1 Give **two** variables that the student should keep constant in this experiment.

....

....

[2]

3.2 Predict what will happen to the level of the solution in Beaker A after 1 hour. Tick **one** box.

It will increase. ☐ It will decrease. ☐ It will stay the same. ☐

[1]

3.3 The level of the solution in Beaker B increased after one hour because there was a net movement of water molecules out of the Visking tubing into the beaker.
Explain why there was a net movement of water molecules out of the Visking tubing.

....

....

[1]

3.4 The level of the solution in Beaker B had stopped increasing by the end of the experiment.
Explain why.

....

....

[2]

[Total 6 marks]

Exam Tip

In your exams, you might be given an experiment you've not done before and have to answer questions about it. If that happens, don't panic. All you need to do is apply what you know about the topic to the new experiment. If there's any extra information that you need to know, it'll be given to you in the question. What a relief.

 ☐  ☐  ☐

Active Transport

1 Glucose molecules can be absorbed from the gut into the blood by active transport. Grade 4-5

1.1 What is active transport?

....

....

[1]

1.2 How are glucose molecules used inside cells?

....

[1]

1.3 Which of these statements about active transport is correct?
Tick **one** box.

It's a type of diffusion. ☐

It can only occur down a concentration gradient. ☐

It needs energy from respiration. ☐

It needs energy from photosynthesis. ☐

[1]

[Total 3 marks]

2 Plants absorb mineral ions from the soil by active transport. Grade 4-5

2.1 Why do plants need mineral ions?

....

[1]

2.2 Why do plants need to use active transport to absorb mineral ions from the soil?

....

....

[2]

2.3 State **two** ways in which active transport differs from diffusion.

1. ....

2. ....

[2]

[Total 5 marks]

Exam Tip

Diffusion, osmosis and active transport can be pretty tricky ideas to get your head around, but it's really important that you do. You could try making a list of all the important facts about each of the three processes and then learning it. Like the fact that active transport needs energy from respiration to happen, but diffusion and osmosis don't.

Exchanging Substances

Warm-Up

Place the following organisms in order according to their surface area to volume ratio.
Number the boxes 1 to 3, with 1 being the smallest and 3 being the largest.

☐ Tiger ☐ Bacterium ☐ Blue whale

1 The cube in **Figure 1** represents a small cell. (Grade 3-4)

Figure 1

1.1 What is the volume of the cube? Tick **one** box.

5 μm^3 ☐ 15 μm^3 ☐

125 μm^3 ☐ 150 μm^3 ☐

[1]

1.2 What is the surface area of the cube? Tick **one** box.

5 μm^2 ☐ 15 μm^2 ☐ 125 μm^2 ☐ 150 μm^2 ☐

[1]

1.3 Another cell has a surface area of 24 μm^2. It has a volume of 8 μm^3.
What is its surface area to volume ratio? Tick **one** box.

3:1 ☐ 2:1 ☐ 1:3 ☐ 1:2 ☐

[1]

[Total 3 marks]

2 **Figure 2** shows the relative sizes of an Arctic hare and a polar bear. Both animals live in cold, snowy conditions. (Grade 4-5)

Figure 2

Having a large surface area to volume ratio increases the rate at which an organism loses heat.
Which of the organisms in **Figure 2** is more likely to have difficulty keeping warm in the Arctic? Explain your answer.

....

....

....

....

[Total 3 marks]

 ☐ 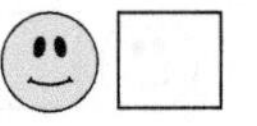 

More on Exchanging Substances

Warm-Up

Which of these are adaptations of a gas exchange surface in animals?
One has been circled for you. Circle **three** more.

a thin membrane | a good blood supply | a thick membrane

being flat | a large surface area (circled) | being ventilated

1 Digested food is absorbed into the blood from the small intestine. Which of the following statements is correct? Tick **one** box. Grade 1-3

Villi decrease the blood supply to the small intestine. ☐

A single layer of surface cells increases the surface area of the small intestine. ☐

Villi increase the surface area of the small intestine. ☐

[Total 1 mark]

2 **Figure 1** shows an alveolus in the lungs. Grade 3-4

Figure 1

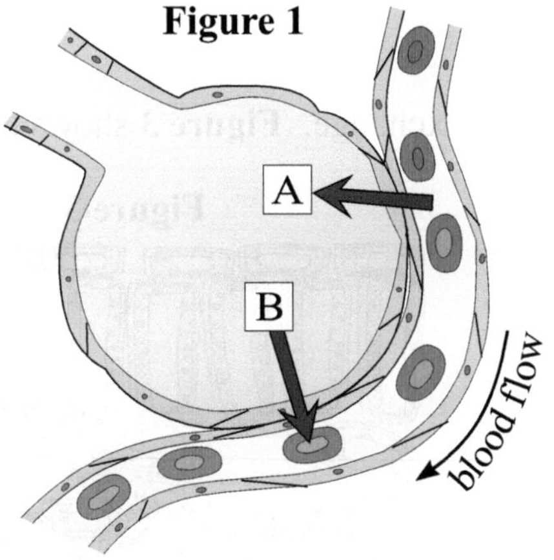

2.1 Name gases A and B.

A ....

B ....

[2]

2.2 By what process do these gases move across the membrane?

....

[1]

2.3 State which feature of the lungs gives:

gases a short distance to move ....

a large surface area ....

[2]

[Total 5 marks]

3 Figure 2 shows a diagram of a fish gill. This is a gas exchange surface.

Figure 2

blood vessels

gill plate

gill filament

gill

3.1 Describe the movement of gases in a fish gill.

....

....

[2]

3.2 The gill filaments and gill plates have the same purpose. Suggest what this purpose is.

....

[1]

3.3 Give **one** other feature of a fish gill. Explain how it makes gas exchange more efficient.

....

....

[2]

[Total 5 marks]

4* Leaves are adapted for gas exchange. **Figure 3** shows the cross-section of a leaf.

Figure 3

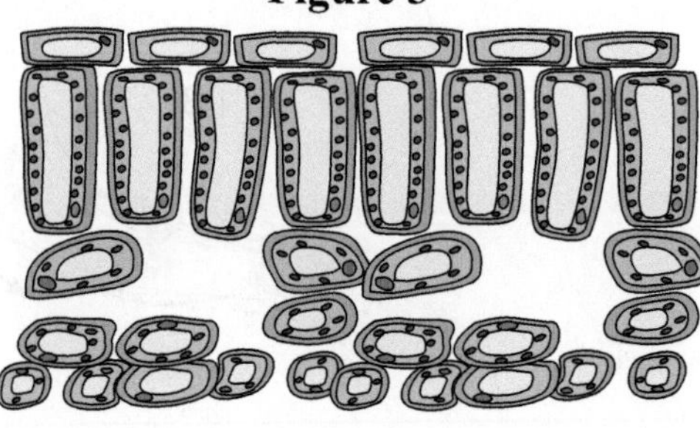

Explain how a leaf is adapted for efficient gas exchange.

....

....

....

....

....

[Total 4 marks]

Exam Tip

There are a fair few exchange surfaces that you need to know about — root hairs and leaves in plants, and gills, villi and alveoli in animals. If you can reel off the ways that exchange surfaces are adapted for exchanging materials, then questions on how the structure of each of these things relates to its function shouldn't catch you out on exam day.

Cell Organisation

Warm-Up

Number the boxes 1 to 4 to put the body components in order of size.
Number 1 should be the smallest component. Number 4 should be the largest component.

☐ Organ system ☐ Tissue ☐ Cell ☐ Organ

1 **Figure 1** is a diagram of the human digestive system. Three organs are labelled **X**, **Y** and **Z**. Grade 4-5

Figure 1

X Y Z

1.1 Draw **one** line to match each letter below to the name of the organ it represents in **Figure 1**.

Letter	**Name of organ**
X	liver
Y	small intestine
Z	large intestine
	stomach

[3]

1.2 What is an organ?

....

....

[1]

1.3 The digestive system is an organ system. What is meant by the term 'organ system'?

....

....

[1]

1.4 Organ systems contain multiple types of tissue. What is a tissue?

....

....

[1]

1.5 What is the role of the digestive system?

....

[1]

[Total 7 marks]

Enzymes

1 The shape of an enzyme is important for its job. **Figure 1** shows an enzyme. Grade 1-3

Figure 1

1.1 Name the part of the enzyme labelled **X** in **Figure 1**.

....

[1]

1.2 The enzyme in **Figure 1** catalyses a reaction that breaks apart a substrate. Which reaction, **A**, **B** or **C**, will the enzyme in **Figure 1** catalyse? Tick **one** box.

A ☐

B ☐

C ☐

[1]

[Total 2 marks]

2 A reaction is catalysed by an enzyme. **Figure 2** shows how temperature affects the rate of this reaction. Grade 4-5

Figure 2

2.1 Look at points **X** and **Y** on **Figure 2**.

Describe the relationship between rate of reaction and temperature between points **X** and **Y**.

....

[1]

2.2 Explain why the reaction has stopped at point **Z**.

....

....

....

[3]

[Total 4 marks]

Exam Tip

Enzymes are important in biology, so it's a pretty good bet that they'll make an appearance on exam day. Make sure you can explain how they work and that you know how temperature and pH affect the rate of enzyme-controlled reactions.

Investigating Enzymatic Reactions

PRACTICAL

1 Amylase is an enzyme. 

1.1 Which of the following statements about amylase is correct?
Tick **one** box.

Amylase joins sugar molecules together to make starch. ☐

Amylase helps to break down sugar into starch. ☐

Amylase helps to break down starch into amino acids. ☐

Amylase helps to break down starch into sugar. ☐

[1]

Iodine solution can be used in investigations into the activity of amylase.

1.2 Describe the colour change that takes place when iodine solution is added to a solution containing starch.

....

....

[2]

[Total 3 marks]

2 A student investigated the effect of pH on amylase activity. Grade 4-5

He added amylase solution to three test tubes, **X**, **Y** and **Z**.
Each test tube contained:
- a starch solution.
- a buffer solution with a different pH.

2.1 Give **one** way that the student could control the temperature in the test tubes.

....

[1]

Table 1 shows how long it took for the reaction in each test tube to finish.

Table 1

Test tube	Time (s)	Rate of reaction
X	110	9.1
Y	40	....
Z	190	....

2.2 Complete **Table 1** to show the rate of the reactions in test tubes **Y** and **Z**.

Use the equation: $\text{Rate} = \frac{1000}{\text{time}}$

Give each of your answers to 2 significant figures.

[2]

2.3 What are the units for the 'Rate of reaction' column in **Table 1**? Tick **one** box.

second (s) ☐ per second (s^{-1}) ☐ time (t) ☐

[1]

[Total 4 marks]

Enzymes and Digestion

1 Enzymes are involved in digestion in the human body. Grade 1-3

1.1 Draw **one or more** lines from each type of molecule to the products of its digestion.

Type of molecule	Products of digestion
carbohydrate	amino acids
lipid	sugars
protein	glycerol
	fatty acids

[4]

1.2 Lipases are digestive enzymes.
What type of molecule do lipases break down? Tick **one** box.

Carbohydrates ☐ Lipids ☐ Proteins ☐

[1]

1.3 Give **two** places in the body that produce lipases.

1. .... 2. ....

[2]

[Total 7 marks]

2 Bile is used in the digestion of fats by enzymes. Grade 3-4

2.1 Complete the sentences below.
Use words from the box.

gall bladder	**small intestine**	**alkaline**	**acidic**
liver	**neutralises**	**emulsifies**	

Bile is produced by the .... It is stored in the ....

It has an .... pH, so it .... acid from the stomach.

It also .... fats.

[5]

2.2 Fats are broken down into tiny droplets before being digested by enzymes.
Why does this make digestion by enzymes happen faster?

....

....

[1]

[Total 6 marks]

Exam Tip

The name of a digestive enzyme usually starts with the same letters as the type of molecule that it breaks down — e.g. proteases break down proteins. Knowing that should make learning their names, and what they do, much easier.

Food Tests

PRACTICAL

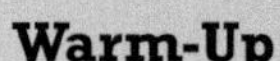

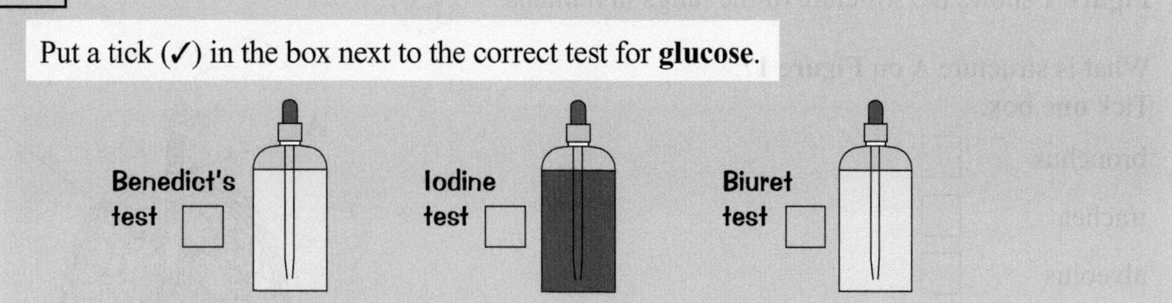

1 Many food tests involve a colour change.

Draw **one** line to match each of the following tests to its positive result.

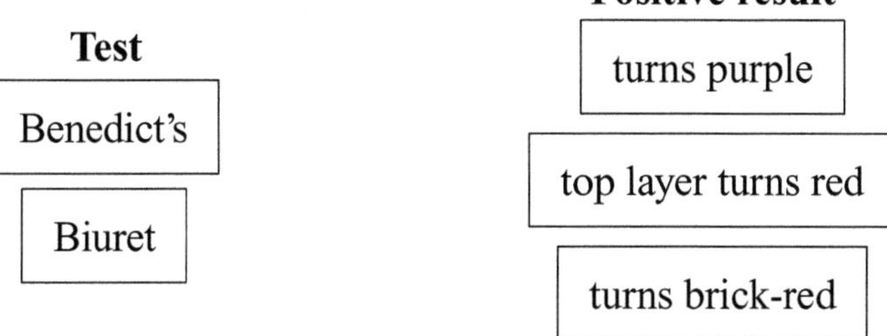

[Total 2 marks]

2* A student has a sample of cooked butter beans.
He wants to find out if the beans contain protein.

Describe how the student could:
- prepare a sample of the beans for testing.
- test for protein in his prepared sample.

....

....

....

....

....

....

....

....

....

....

....

[Total 6 marks]

Exam Tip

When you get a long-answer question, it's OK to use spare space on your exam paper to jot down the key points you want to make before you start writing. Just remember to cross your jottings out afterwards so they don't get marked.

The Lungs

1 **Figure 1** shows the structure of the lungs in humans. Grade 1-3

Figure 1

1.1 What is structure **A** on **Figure 1**?
Tick **one** box.

bronchus ☐

trachea ☐

alveolus ☐

[1]

1.2 What is structure **B** on **Figure 1**?
Tick **one** box.

bronchus ☐ trachea ☐ alveolus ☐

[1]

[Total 2 marks]

2 A student ran for 12 minutes.
During this 12 minute run, the student took 495 breaths. Grade 3-4

Calculate the student's average breathing rate.
Use the equation: breathing rate = number of breaths ÷ number of minutes

Give your answer to 3 significant figures.

.... breaths per minute

[Total 2 marks]

3 **Figure 2** shows an alveolus surrounded by a capillary.
Table 1 shows the relative concentrations of oxygen and carbon dioxide at positions **X**, **Y** and **Z** in **Figure 2**.

Complete **Table 1** by writing **high** or **low** in the empty cells.

Table 1

	Oxygen concentration	Carbon dioxide concentration
X	High	Low
Y	Low	....
Z	....	....

[Total 3 marks]

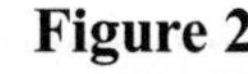

Figure 2

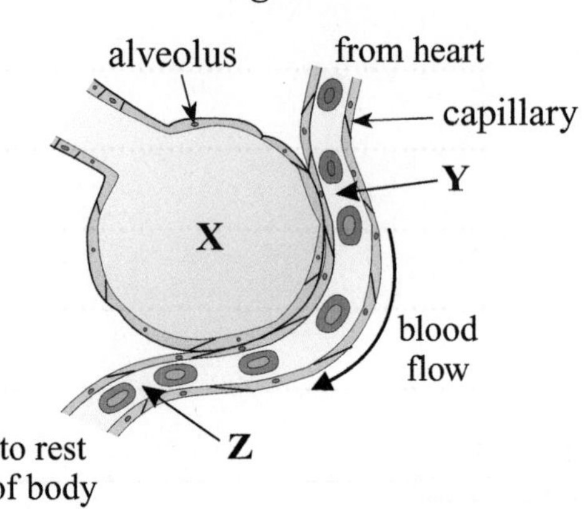

Circulatory System — The Heart

1 Figure 1 shows a diagram of the heart. Grade 1-3

Figure 1

1.1 What is the part of the heart labelled **X**? Tick **one** box.

vena cava ☐

pulmonary artery ☐

aorta ☐

[1]

The arrows on **Figure 1** show the direction of blood flow through the **left side** of the heart.

1.2 Which of the following answers should be used to complete the sentence? Write the correct letter, **A**, **B** or **C** in the box below.

A vena cava

B pulmonary artery

C aorta

The left ventricle pumps blood through the ☐ to cells all over the body.

[1]

1.3 Draw arrows on **Figure 1** to show the direction of blood flow through the **right side** of the heart.

[1]

[Total 3 marks]

2 The heart has a pacemaker. Grade 3-4

2.1 Which of these statements about the pacemaker is true? Tick **one** box.

It is found in the left atrium. ☐

It keeps blood flowing in the right direction. ☐

It controls the resting heart rate. ☐

It supplies the heart muscle with blood. ☐

[1]

2.2 Suggest why someone might need to be given an artificial pacemaker.

....

[1]

[Total 2 marks]

3 Explain why the human circulatory system is described as a 'double circulatory system'. Grade 4-5

....

....

....

....

....

[Total 3 marks]

☐ ☐ ☐

Circulatory System — Blood Vessels

1 **Figure 1** shows the three types of blood vessel.

Figure 1

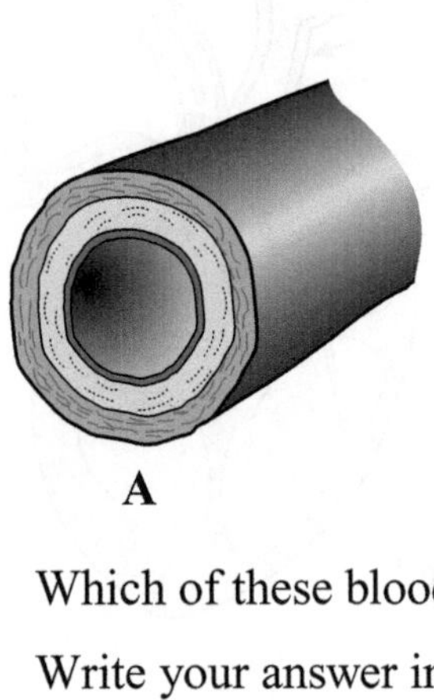

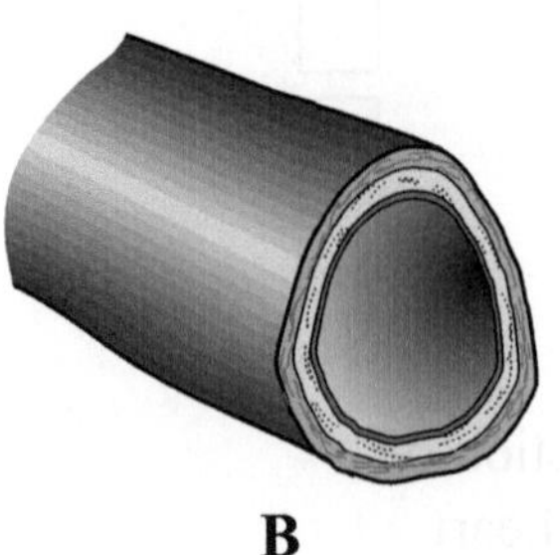

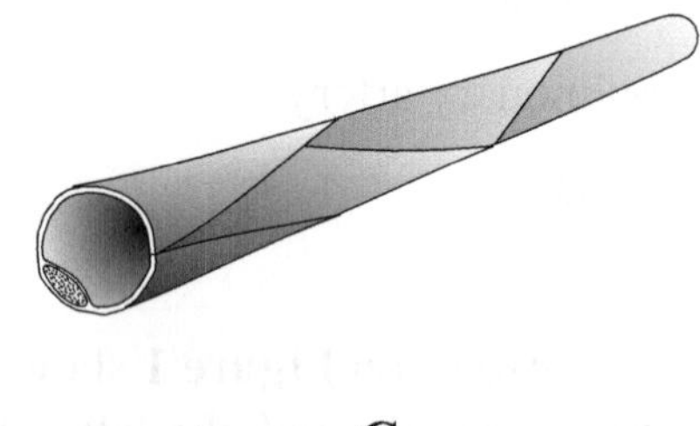

Which of these blood vessels, **A**, **B** or **C**, is an artery?

Write your answer in the box. ☐

Give a reason for your answer.

....

....

[Total 2 marks]

2 Different types of blood vessel have different structures and functions.

2.1 Complete **Table 1** to show whether each feature is part of a capillary, an artery or a vein.
Put a tick in each row.

Table 1

Feature	Capillary	Artery	Vein
Elastic fibres in blood vessel walls			
Large lumen			
Thin walls, with gaps between the cells			
Valves			

[3]

2.2 Describe the function of capillaries.

....

....

[2]

2.3 Explain why arteries have a different structure to veins.

....

....

....

[2]

[Total 7 marks]

Target AO3

3 An experiment was carried out to investigate how elastic arteries and veins are.

The experiment was set up as shown in **Figure 2**.
The method used was as follows:

1. Cut a ring of tissue from an artery, measure the width and then attach it to the hook.
2. Attach a mass carrier to the bottom of the ring.
3. Measure the length of the ring with the mass carrier attached.
4. Add a 10 g mass to the mass carrier.
5. Measure the length of the ring with the mass attached, and then again with the mass removed.
6. Repeat steps 4 and 5 with a 20 g mass, 30 g mass, etc.
7. Repeat the experiment using a ring of vein of the same width.

Figure 2

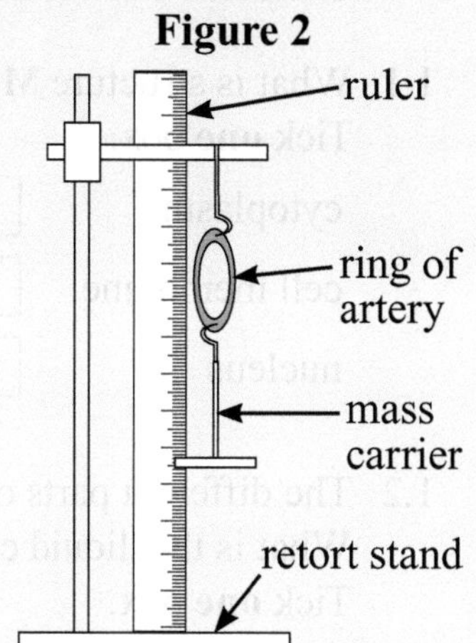

The percentage change between the original length of the ring with just the mass carrier attached and its length after each mass was removed was calculated for each mass. The results are plotted in **Figure 3**.

Figure 3

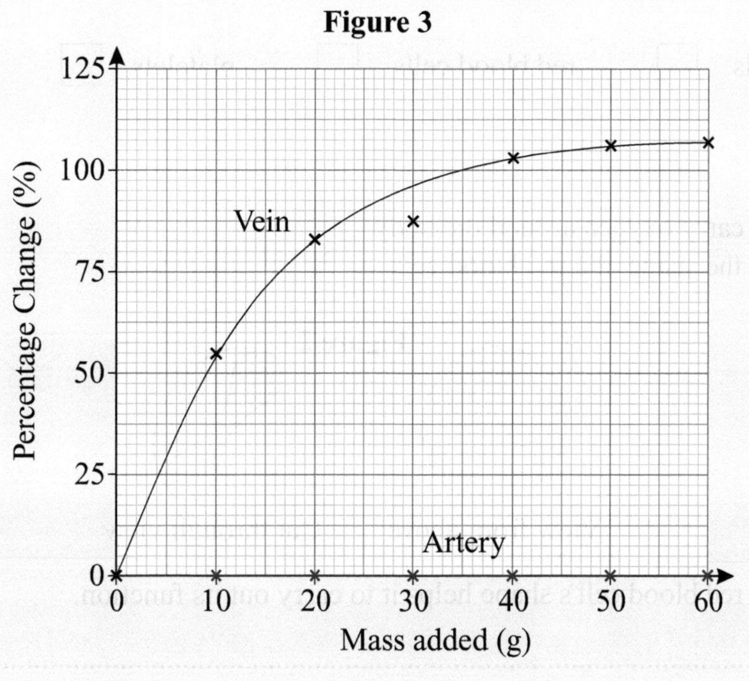

3.1 Based on the results in **Figure 3**, which of the following statements is correct?
Tick **one** box.

The greater the mass added to the vein, the less it stretched. ☐

The artery returned to its original length when the mass was removed. ☐

The ring of vein was shorter at the end of the experiment than it was at the start. ☐

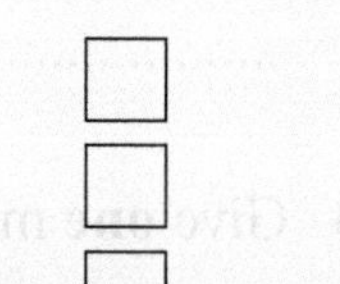

[1]

3.2 There is an anomalous result in **Figure 3**.
Suggest **one** reason why this anomalous result may have occurred.

....

[1]

[Total 2 marks]

Circulatory System — Blood

1 The blood has several different parts. **Figure 1** shows a white blood cell. Grade 1-3

1.1 What is structure **M** on **Figure 1**?
Tick **one** box.

cytoplasm ☐
cell membrane ☐
nucleus ☐

[1]

Figure 1

1.2 The different parts of the blood are carried in a liquid.
What is this liquid called?
Tick **one** box.

plasma ☐ cell sap ☐ urine ☐ bile ☐

[1]

1.3 Which of the following parts of the blood is responsible for clotting?
Tick **one** box.

white blood cells ☐ red blood cells ☐ platelets ☐ antibodies ☐

[1]

[Total 3 marks]

2 Red blood cells carry oxygen around the body.
Figure 2 shows the shape of a red blood cell. Grade 3-4

Figure 2

2.1 Describe how a red blood cell's shape helps it to carry out its function.

....

[1]

2.2 Red blood cells don't have a nucleus. How does this help them to carry out their function?

....

[1]

2.3 Give **one** more feature of red blood cells that help them to carry out their function.

....

[1]

[Total 3 marks]

Exam Tip

A lot of the easier marks in the exam come from just knowing your facts inside out — like in Question 1 on this page. Having that key knowledge under your belt will make all the difference on exam day. You'll also feel more confident tackling the harder questions in the exam if you know you've got the answers to some of the easier ones right already.

Cardiovascular Disease

Warm-Up

Fill in the gaps to complete the following sentence. Choose **two** of the words below.

lungs   blood vessels   heart   legs

Cardiovascular diseases are diseases of the ....

and the ....

1 Statins are drugs that can be used to prevent cardiovascular diseases. (Grade 3-4)

1.1 What do statins do?
Tick **one** box.

They lower the blood cholesterol level. ☐

They increase the blood cholesterol level. ☐

They remove all cholesterol from the blood. ☐

[1]

1.2 Give **one** disadvantage of using statins to prevent cardiovascular diseases.

....

....

[1]

[Total 2 marks]

2 Heart attacks happen when the heart muscle does not get enough oxygen. (Grade 4-5)

2.1 Explain how **stents** prevent heart attacks from happening.

....

....

....

[2]

2.2 A doctor is advising a patient about having a stent fitted.
Give **one** risk that the doctor is likely to tell the patient about.

....

....

[1]

[Total 3 marks]

More on Cardiovascular Disease

1 A man has a leaky heart valve. (Grade 4-5)

1.1 Which statement about leaky heart valves is correct?
Tick **one** box.

Leaky heart valves increase blood flow through the heart. ☐

Leaky heart valves stop blood flowing through the heart. ☐

Leaky heart valves allow blood to flow in both directions through the heart. ☐

Leaky heart valves do not affect blood flow through the heart. ☐

[1]

1.2 Apart from being leaky, describe **one** other way that a valve might be faulty.

....

[1]

1.3 Suggest **one** way in which the man's surgeons could treat the leaky valve.

....

....

[1]

[Total 3 marks]

2 A patient is having a heart transplant. (Grade 4-5)

2.1 Why might a patient need a heart transplant?

....

[1]

A donor heart can be transplanted into a patient, or an artificial heart may be used instead.

Donor hearts come from a person who has recently died.
Artificial hearts are machines made from metal or plastic.

2.2 Suggest **one** advantage of using an artificial heart over a donor heart.

....

....

[1]

2.3 Suggest **one** disadvantage of using an artificial heart over a donor heart.

....

....

[1]

[Total 3 marks]

Exam Tip

There are quite a few different ways of treating cardiovascular disease that you need to know about for your exam. As well as knowing what they are and how they work, make sure you can discuss their advantages and disadvantages.

Health and Disease

1 Diseases can lead to poor health. (Grade 3-4)

1.1 What is health?

....

[1]

1.2 List **two** factors other than disease that can cause poor health.

1. ....

2. ....

[2]

1.3 What is the difference between a communicable disease and a non-communicable disease? Tick **one** box.

- [ ] They are caused by different types of pathogens.
- [ ] Only communicable diseases can spread between people.
- [ ] Only non-communicable diseases can spread between people.

[1]

[Total 4 marks]

2 AIDS is a disease caused by a virus.
People with AIDS have a weakened immune system. (Grade 4-5)

2.1 Explain why a person with AIDS is likely to get other diseases.

....

....

[2]

2.2 Give **one** other example of how different diseases can interact.

....

....

[1]

2.3 The virus that causes AIDS can be passed between people during sexual intercourse.

Is AIDS a communicable or non-communicable disease?
Give a reason for your answer.

....

....

[1]

[Total 4 marks]

Risk Factors for Non-Communicable Diseases

1 Substances in a person's environment can be risk factors for certain diseases. Grade 4-5

1.1 What is meant by a risk factor for a disease?

....

....

[1]

1.2 Other than substances in the environment, state **two** types of risk factor.

1. ....

2. ....

[2]

1.3 Obesity is a risk factor for many different diseases.
Name **one** disease that obesity is a risk factor for.

....

[1]

[Total 4 marks]

2 A patient has been diagnosed with cardiovascular disease. Grade 4-5

2.1 Give **two** risk factors that might have contributed to the patient developing cardiovascular disease.

1. ....

2. ....

[2]

2.2 Suggest **one** reason why non-communicable diseases can be expensive for an individual.

....

....

[1]

2.3 Suggest **one** reason why non-communicable diseases can be expensive for a country.

....

....

[1]

[Total 4 marks]

Exam Tip

Scientists find risk factors by looking for correlations (relationships) in data. Many risk factors don't directly cause a disease, but they do make it more likely. A person is even more likely to get a disease if they have several risk factors for it.

Target AO3

3 **Figure 1** shows the prevalence of adult obesity in England, between 2012 and 2018. **Figure 2** shows the number of people diagnosed with diabetes in England, between 2012 and 2018.

Figure 1

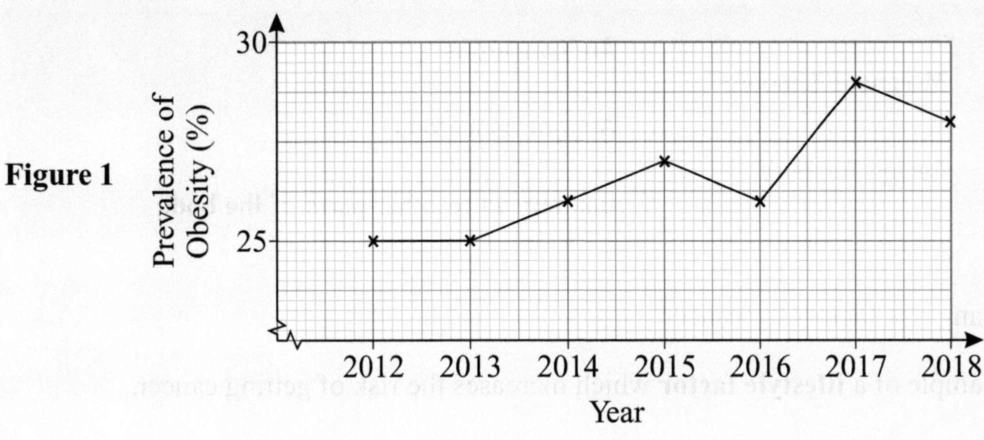

Figure 2

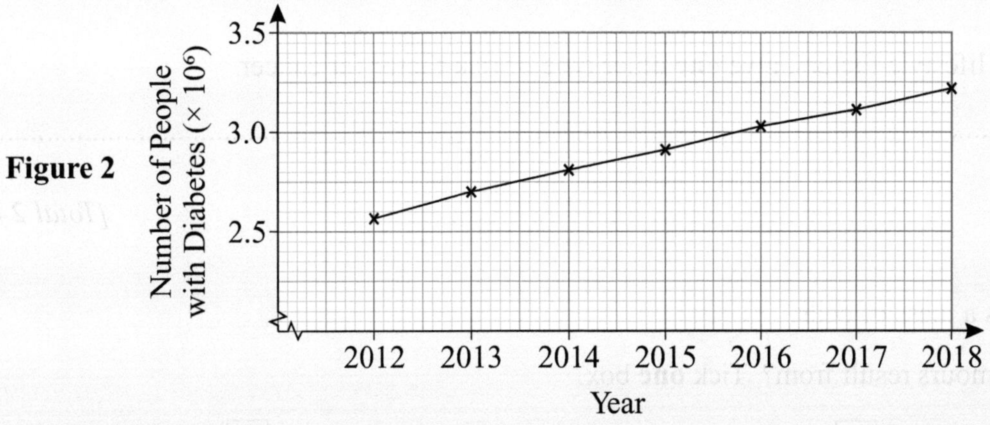

3.1 Give **one** similarity and **one** difference between the trends shown in **Figures 1** and **2**.

Similarity: ....

....

Difference: ....

....

[2]

3.2 A student says: "the increasing rate of obesity has caused the rate of diabetes to increase". Give **one** reason why this is not a valid conclusion based on the data in **Figures 1** and **2**.

....

....

[1]

[Total 3 marks]

Exam Tip

You've got to be really careful with the conclusions you make about data you're given — they need to match the data and not go beyond it. So have a close look at all the information you get and don't jump to conclusions too quickly.

Cancer

Warm-Up

Tumours can be benign or malignant. Draw lines to match the types of tumour on the left with each characteristic on the right that applies to them.

Malignant Tumours	Are cancerous
Benign Tumours	Are not cancerous
	Can spread to other parts of the body

1 There are many risk factors for cancer. Grade 3-4

1.1 Give **one** example of a **lifestyle factor** which increases the risk of getting cancer.

....

[1]

1.2 Apart from lifestyle factors, give **one** other type of risk factor for cancer.

....

[1]

[Total 2 marks]

2 A tumour is a mass of cells. Grade 4-5

2.1 What do tumours result from? Tick **one** box.

Rapid cell death ☐ No cell division ☐

Slow cell division ☐ Uncontrolled cell division ☐

[1]

Figure 1 shows two tumours in a person's body.
The secondary tumour was formed from the original tumour.

Figure 1

secondary tumour

original tumour

2.2 Explain how secondary tumours form in the body.

....

....

....

....

[2]

[Total 3 marks]

Exam Tip

The terms 'malignant tumour' and 'benign tumour' are really easy to get mixed up. Check you got the answer to the Warm-Up question on this page right. If you didn't, take the time to go and learn what these two terms mean. Cancer might not be the nicest topic in the world, but that doesn't mean there won't be exam questions on it.

 ☐  ☐  ☐

Plant Cell Organisation

1 Leaves have many different types of tissue. (Grade 1-3)

1.1 Draw **one** line to match each tissue on the left with its function on the right.

Tissue	Function
epidermal	transports water into the leaf
meristem	covers the upper and lower surface of the leaf
xylem	absorbs water from the soil
	causes growth at the tips of roots and shoots

[3]

1.2 Which of the following answers should be used to complete the sentence?
Write the correct letter, **A**, **B** or **C**, in the box below.

A organ

B organ system

C tissue system

A leaf is an example of a plant ☐ .

[1]

[Total 4 marks]

2 **Figure 1** shows a diagram of a palisade cell. (Grade 4-5)

Figure 1

2.1 Explain why most palisade cells are found near the top of a leaf.

....

....

[2]

2.2 Give **one** way in which the structure of a palisade cell helps it to carry out its function.

....

[1]

2.3 Name a tissue inside the leaf that is specialised for gas exchange.

....

[1]

[Total 4 marks]

Transpiration and Translocation

Warm-Up

The diagrams show a phloem tube and a xylem tube.
In the spaces, write down which one is the phloem tube and which one is the xylem tube.

A: .... B: ....

1 Xylem and phloem transport substances through a plant. Grade 1-3

1.1 What does the xylem transport?
Tick **two** boxes.

mineral ions ☐ protein ☐ sugar ☐ water ☐ starch ☐

[2]

1.2 Which statement about transport in the phloem is correct?
Tick **one** box.

It only occurs in the leaves. ☐

It is called transpiration. ☐

It moves sugar around the plant. ☐

It only moves substances upwards from the roots. ☐

[1]

[Total 3 marks]

2 Complete the following passage by filling in the blanks. Grade 3-4

Use words from the box. Each word can only be used once.

transpiration	**translocation**	**condensation**	**evaporation**

The process by which water is lost from a plant is called ....

It is caused by the .... and diffusion of water from a plant's surface.

The transport of sugars around the plant is called ....

[Total 3 marks]

Exam Tip

It can be tricky to remember which is which when thinking of xylem and phloem. They're pretty similar and they've both got weird names. If you're struggling to remember, keep practising these questions. It will soon stick in your head.

Transpiration and Stomata

1 **Figure 1** shows what the surface of a leaf looks like under a microscope.

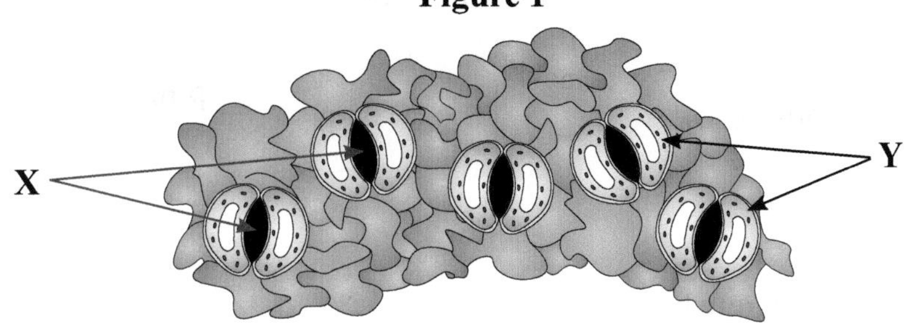

1.1 Name the structures labelled **X** and **Y** in **Figure 1**.

X .... **Y** ....

[2]

1.2 What is the function of the structures labelled **Y**?

....

....

[2]

[Total 4 marks]

2 Some students were investigating the effect of air flow on the rate of transpiration. To do so, they measured the water uptake of a plant in still and moving air. The rate of water uptake is assumed to be equal to the transpiration rate.

Grade 4-5

Table 1 shows the students' results.

Table 1

	Repeat	1	2	3	4	5	Mean
Water uptake in 30 minutes (cm^3)	Still Air	1.2	1.2	1.0	0.8	1.1	1.1
	Moving Air	2.0	1.8	2.3	1.9	1.7	**X**

2.1 Calculate the value of **X** in **Table 1**.
Give your answer to 2 significant figures.

X = ... cm^3

[2]

2.2 Describe the relationship between air flow around the plant and transpiration rate.

....

[1]

2.3 Explain the effect of air flow on the rate of transpiration.

....

....

....

[2]

[Total 5 marks]

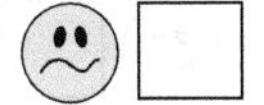

Communicable Disease

Warm-Up

Circle the word below which is **not** a type of pathogen.

bacteria viruses insects fungi protists

1 What is a pathogen? Tick **one** box. Grade 1-3

A type of disease. ☐

A microorganism that causes disease. ☐

Something used to prevent the spread of disease. ☐

Something used to treat a disease. ☐

[Total 1 mark]

2 There are different ways to prevent or reduce the spread of disease. Grade 3-4

2.1 Vectors are organisms that spread disease.
Give **one** way that vectors can be stopped from passing on diseases.

....

....

[1]

2.2 Give **one** other way that humans can help prevent the spread of a disease.

....

[1]

[Total 2 marks]

3 Oliver has the common cold.
The common cold is a communicable disease. Grade 4-5

3.1 What is meant by the term 'communicable disease'?

....

[1]

3.2 Oliver uses a tissue when he coughs and sneezes.
Suggest how this helps to prevent others from catching his cold.

....

....

[2]

[Total 3 marks]

Bacterial Diseases

1 *Salmonella* food poisoning in humans is caused by a type of bacterium. Grade 4-5

1.1 Symptoms of *Salmonella* food poisoning include fever and vomiting.
What substances are produced by *Salmonella* bacteria that cause these symptoms?

....

[1]

1.2 Give **two** ways that somebody could get *Salmonella* food poisoning.

1. ....

2. ....

[2]

1.3 In the UK, poultry are vaccinated against *Salmonella*. Why it is important to vaccinate poultry?

....

....

....

[2]

[Total 5 marks]

2 Gonorrhoea is a disease that can affect both men and women. Grade 4-5

2.1 How is gonorrhoea spread from person to person?

....

[1]

2.2 State **two** symptoms of the disease in women.

1. ....

2. ....

[2]

2.3 Name the antibiotic that was previously used to treat people infected with gonorrhoea.

....

[1]

2.4 Why is the antibiotic in **2.3** no longer able to effectively treat gonorrhoea?

....

[1]

2.5 Name **one** barrier method of contraception that prevents the spread of gonorrhoea.

....

[1]

[Total 6 marks]

Exam Tip

You'll often get questions that tell you how many things you need to include in your answer. Double-check that you've written the right number of things before you move on. There's no way you can get full marks if you don't write enough.

Viral Diseases

1 Measles is a highly infectious disease. Grade 1-3

1.1 What are the symptoms of measles?
Tick **two** boxes.

fever ☐ constipation ☐ yellow discharge ☐ red skin rash ☐ painful urination ☐

[2]

1.2 What can be given to prevent someone from developing measles?
Tick **one** box.

antibiotics ☐ antiretrovirals ☐ a vaccination ☐ aspirin ☐

[1]

[Total 3 marks]

2 The tobacco mosaic virus (TMV) affects many species of plants. Grade 3-4

2.1 Name **one** species of plant that can be attacked by the tobacco mosaic virus.

....

[1]

2.2 Which of the following plants, **A**, **B** or **C**, is infected with TMV?

Your answer = ...

[1]

[Total 2 marks]

3 A virus called HIV causes a disease known as AIDS. Grade 4-5

3.1 What type of drug can be used to control HIV?

....

[1]

3.2 What system in the body does HIV attack?

....

[1]

3.3 Describe how viruses such as HIV cause cell damage.

....

....

[2]

[Total 4 marks]

Fungal and Protist Diseases

Warm-Up

Fill in the gaps in the passage about malaria. Use words on the left.
Not all of the words will be used.

protist
fungus
fever
vectors

Malaria is caused by a ....

Mosquitoes are the .... that carry the malaria pathogen to humans.

Malaria causes repeating episodes of ....

1 **Figure 1** shows a rose plant affected by a fungal disease. 

Figure 1

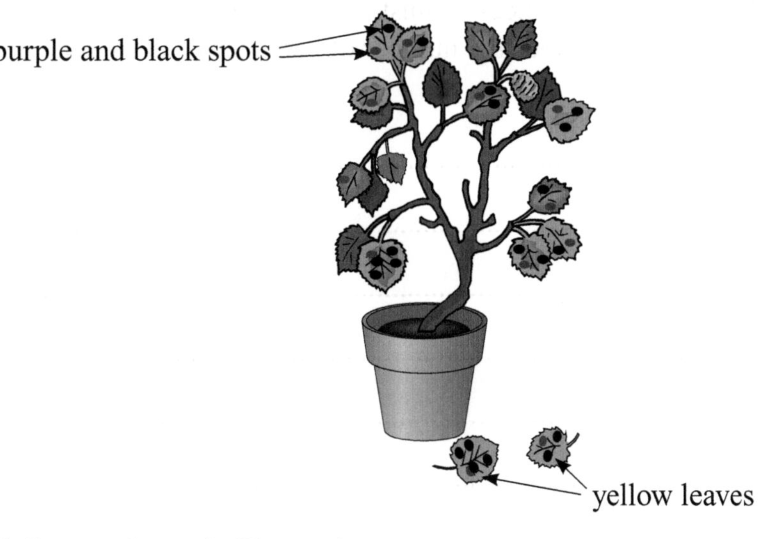

1.1 Name the fungal disease shown in **Figure 1**.

....

[1]

A gardener notices that one of her rose plants has the disease shown in **Figure 1**.
She is worried that the rest of her rose plants may also become infected.

1.2 Give **one** way that the disease could spread to other rose plants in her garden.

....

[1]

1.3 Describe how the gardener could treat the disease and stop it from spreading.

....

....

....

[3]

[Total 5 marks]

Fighting Disease

1 Different types of white blood cell have different roles in the immune system.

Complete the sentences below. Use words from the box.

phagocytosis	dissolve	antitoxins	antibodies	digest

Some white blood cells engulf and .... pathogens.
This is called ....

Other white blood cells produce proteins that lock onto invading pathogens.

These proteins are called ....

[Total 3 marks]

2* The human body has several defences against the entry of pathogens.
Explain how these defences reduce the number of pathogens entering the body.

Grade 4-5

....

....

....

....

....

....

....

....

....

....

....

....

....

[Total 6 marks]

Exam Tip

Don't panic when you get to a 6-mark question in the exams. Read the question through carefully, then stop and think before you answer. First work out what the question is asking you to write about. Then write down the points you want to make, in an order that makes sense. And make sure that you've made enough points to get all of the marks.

Fighting Disease — Vaccination

Warm-Up

Why are people given vaccinations? Underline the correct answer.

To help them get better if they are already ill.

To make them less likely to get ill in the future.

To get rid of their symptoms.

1 Children are often vaccinated against measles.

1.1 What is usually injected into the body during a vaccination?
Tick **one** box.

antibiotics ☐

antibodies ☐

dead or inactive pathogens ☐

active pathogens ☐

[1]

1.2 How should a child's white blood cells respond to a vaccination?

....

[1]

[Total 2 marks]

2 Two children become infected with the measles pathogen.
One child has been vaccinated against measles and the other has not.

Figure 1 shows how the concentration of the measles antibody in each child's bloodstream changes after infection with the measles pathogen.

Figure 1

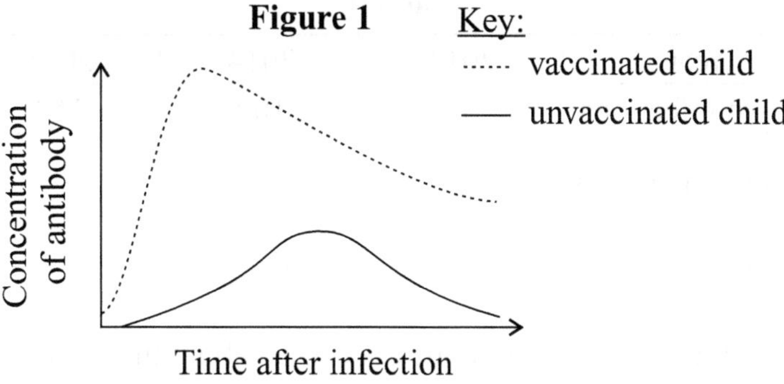

Using **Figure 1**, describe how antibody production differs between the vaccinated child and the unvaccinated child.

....

....

....

[Total 2 marks]

Fighting Disease — Drugs

Warm-Up

Complete each sentence below by ticking the correct box.

Digitalis is a drug used to treat ☐ heart conditions ☐ lung conditions

Digitalis was made from a chemical found in ☐ daisies ☐ foxgloves

1 A student has a sore throat. Her doctor says it is caused by a virus. (Grade 3-4)

1.1 The student says: "My sore throat cannot be treated with antibiotics."
Is the student correct? Give a reason for your answer.

....

....

[1]

1.2 Name a type of drug that the student could use to reduce her symptoms.

....

[1]

[Total 2 marks]

2 A hospital records the number of cases of infections that are caused by antibiotic-resistant bacteria each year. The figures for three years are shown in **Table 1**. (Grade 4-5)

Table 1

Year	2013	2014	2015
No. of infections	84	102	153

2.1 Describe the trend shown in **Table 1**.

....

[1]

2.2 Suggest why doctors in the hospital might be concerned about the trend shown in **Table 1**.

....

....

[2]

[Total 3 marks]

Exam Tip

If a question asks you to 'describe the trend', it just means 'look at the data and say what patterns you can see in it'.

Developing Drugs

1 New drugs have to undergo preclinical testing and clinical testing before they can be used. Grade 4-5

1.1 Which of the following is preclinical testing carried out on?
Tick **one** box.

healthy human volunteers ☐

cells, tissues and dead animals ☐

patients in a hospital ☐

cells, tissues and live animals ☐

[1]

1.2 During preclinical testing, scientists test a drug to find out whether it works.
Give **two** more things that the drug is tested for during preclinical testing.

1. ....

2. ....

[2]

During clinical testing, patients are split into two groups.
One group is given the drug. Another group is given a placebo.

1.3 What is a placebo?

....

[1]

1.4 Explain why some patients are given the drug and others are given a placebo.

....

....

[2]

1.5 Which of the following answers should be used to complete the sentence?
Write the correct letter, **A**, **B** or **C**, in the box below.

A only the patients

B only the doctors

C both the patients and the doctors

In a double blind trial, ☐ involved in the trial don't know who is receiving the placebo.

[1]

[Total 7 marks]

Exam Tip

There's a lot going on when it comes to drug development. The best way to learn it all is to write out each step of the process in order, in as much detail as you can. Keep going over the information till it sticks. Then, if you're asked a question about the development of a particular drug in the exam, it's just a case of applying what you know.

Plant Diseases and Defences

1 Plants need a range of mineral ions to stay healthy. Grade 3-4

1.1 Which of the following statements about nitrate ions are correct?
Tick **two** boxes.

A lack of nitrate ions causes stunted growth. ☐

Nitrate ions don't affect plant growth. ☐

Too many nitrate ions cause stunted growth. ☐

Nitrate ions are needed to make proteins. ☐

[2]

Plants also need magnesium ions.

1.2 Why do plants need magnesium ions?

....

[1]

1.3 Describe the physical appearance of a plant with a magnesium deficiency.

....

[1]

[Total 4 marks]

2 Plants have many ways of defending themselves. Grade 4-5

2.1 Give **two** types of chemical that plants can produce for defence.

1. ....

2. ....

[2]

2.2 Explain how physical defences help plants to defend themselves.

....

[1]

2.3 Some plants have mechanical defences to defend themselves against damage caused by insects.
Name **one** insect that can cause damage to plants.

....

[1]

2.4 State **one** type of mechanical defence that helps plants to protect themselves.

....

[1]

2.5 Explain how the mechanical defence you named in **2.4** works.

....

....

[1]

[Total 6 marks]

Target AO3

3 A student wanted to investigate how mineral ion deficiencies affect plant growth.

- The student planted 20 radish seedlings in a growth medium deficient in magnesium.
- As a control experiment, he also planted 20 radish seedlings in a growth medium containing a complete supply of minerals.
- He left all the plants to grow for 20 days.
- Then he measured the total mass of each group of plants.

The student's results are shown in **Figure 1**.

Figure 1

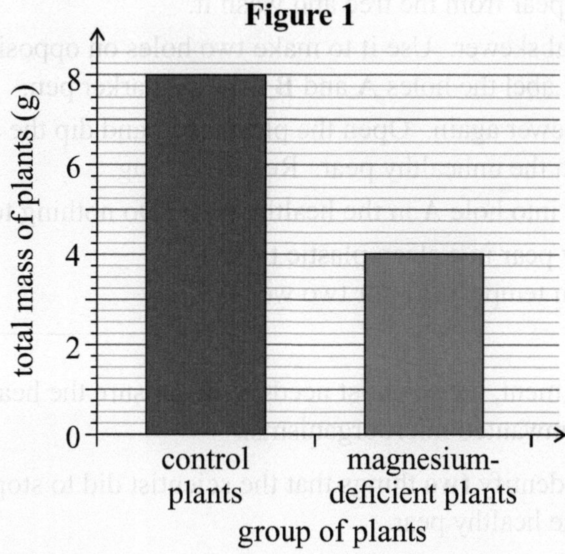

3.1 Describe the results of the student's experiment, as shown in **Figure 1**.

....

....
[1]

3.2 The plants were all grown for the same length of time (20 days).
Give **one** other thing the student should have kept constant.

....
[1]

3.3 What was the **dependent variable** in the student's experiment?

....
[1]

3.4 The student reads that plants which lack phosphate ions often have fewer leaves than plants with a complete mineral supply. He wants to know if this is true for radish plants.

The student decides to investigate this by doing another experiment using a similar method to his first one. Give **two** things in the method that he will need to change for his new investigation.

1. ....

....

2. ....

....
[2]

[Total 5 marks]

Target AO3

4 A scientist has a pear tree. She notices that some of the pears on the tree have brown patches on them. She decides to perform an experiment to work out if the damage is being caused by a pathogen. Her method is shown below.

Method

1) Pick a pear with a brown patch on it and seal it in a plastic bag. Wash your hands.
2) Pick a healthy pear from the tree and wash it.
3) Sterilise a metal skewer. Use it to make two holes on opposite sides of the healthy pear. Label the holes **A** and **B** using a marker pen.
4) Sterilise the skewer again. Open the plastic bag and dip the skewer into the brown patch on the unhealthy pear. Reseal the bag.
5) Put the skewer into hole **A** in the healthy pear. Do nothing to hole **B**.
6) Put the healthy pear in a clean plastic tub.
   Keep it at room temperature for two weeks.

As she does the experiment, the scientist needs to make sure the healthy pear is not contaminated by any unwanted microorganisms.

4.1 Look at the method. Identify **two** things that the scientist did to stop unwanted pathogens from contaminating the healthy pear.

1. ....

2. ....

[2]

After two weeks, the scientist looks at hole **A** and hole **B** on the pear and records what she sees.

4.2 Describe what you would expect the scientist to see when she looks at each hole if the brown patches are caused by a plant pathogen.

Hole **A**: ....

....

Hole **B**: ....

....

[2]

4.3 Describe what the scientist should do to show that her results are **repeatable**.

....

....

[1]

[Total 5 marks]

Exam Tip

Don't worry if you get asked questions in your exam about the method of an experiment that you haven't come across before. You won't be asked anything that you can't figure out based on your knowledge of the subject and of the practical work that you've done during the course. Of course that does mean you'll actually have to pay attention in practicals...

Photosynthesis

1 Plants produce glucose during photosynthesis. The glucose is then used to make other substances, which have their own uses.

1.1 The words on the left are all substances made using glucose.
Draw **one** line from each substance to its use.

Substance made using glucose	**Use**
starch	storage
fats and oils	making proteins
amino acids	making cell walls
cellulose	storage
	making DNA

[4]

1.2 What else is glucose used for in plant cells?

....

[1]

[Total 5 marks]

2 Photosynthesis takes place inside plant cells.

2.1 Name the subcellular structures where photosynthesis takes place.

....

[1]

2.2 Complete the following word equation for photosynthesis.

.... + water → glucose + ...

[2]

2.3 Which of the following statements is correct?
Tick **one** box.

Energy is transferred from the environment during photosynthesis. ☐

Energy is transferred to the environment during photosynthesis. ☐

Energy is made during photosynthesis. ☐

Energy is broken down during photosynthesis. ☐

[1]

[Total 4 marks]

The Rate of Photosynthesis

Warm-Up

Which of the following things limit the rate of photosynthesis?
Circle the **four** correct answers.

carbon dioxide concentration | amount of soil | amount of glucose
light intensity | temperature | amount of chlorophyll

1 An experiment was done to test the effect of increasing the carbon dioxide concentration on the rate of photosynthesis. The results are shown in **Figure 1**.

Figure 1

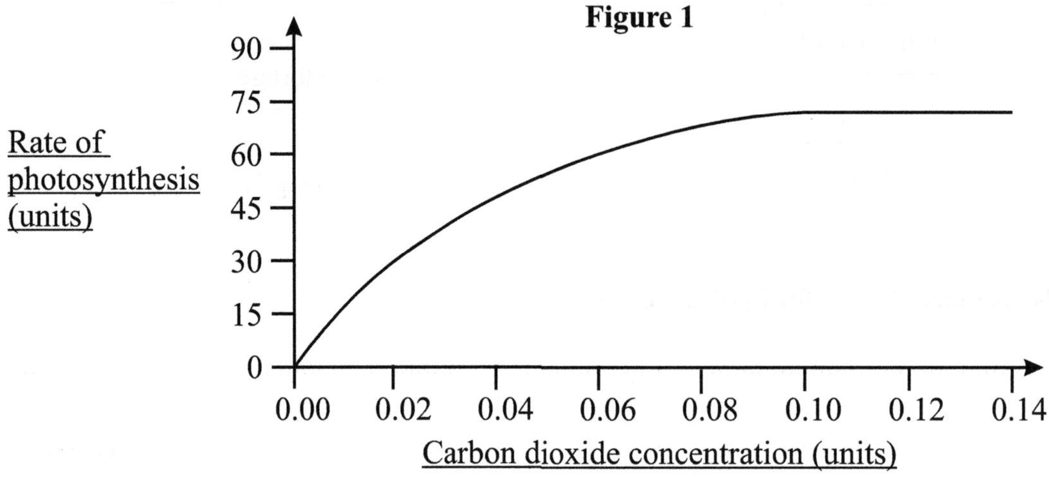

1.1 What conclusion can be drawn from the data in **Figure 1**?
Tick **one** box.

Carbon dioxide becomes a limiting factor at a concentration of 0.10 units. ☐

Carbon dioxide stops being a limiting factor at a concentration of 0.10 units. ☐

Carbon dioxide is a limiting factor at all concentrations. ☐

[1]

1.2 At a carbon dioxide concentration of **0.02 units**, the rate of photosynthesis was **30 units**.
At what carbon dioxide concentration had the rate of photosynthesis **doubled**?
Tick **one** box.

0.00 units ☐ 0.04 units ☐ 0.06 units ☐ 0.08 units ☐

[1]

[Total 2 marks]

Exam Tip

You might need to read a value off a graph in the exam. If so, you'll need to get your ruler out. For example, imagine you were asked to use the graph above to find the rate of photosynthesis at a carbon dioxide concentration of 0.02 units. You'd find 0.02 units on the bottom axis and use a ruler to draw a straight line up from there to the line of the graph. Then you'd draw a straight line across to the 'rate of photosynthesis' axis and read off the value there (30 units).

2 A student did an experiment to see how the rate of photosynthesis depends on light intensity. She measured the volume of oxygen produced by pondweed at different intensities of light. **Table 1** shows her results. **Figure 2** shows some of her apparatus.

Table 1

Relative light intensity	1	2	3	4	5	6	7	8	9	10
Volume of oxygen produced in 10 minutes (cm^3)	8	12	18	25	31	13	42	48	56	61

2.1 State the dependent variable and the independent variable in this experiment.

Dependent variable: ....

Independent variable: ....

[2]

Figure 2

oxygen bubbles

LIGHT SOURCE

pondweed

2.2 State **two** factors that should be kept constant during this experiment.

1. ....

2. ....

[2]

2.3 **Figure 3** is a graph showing the student's results.
Complete the graph using the results from **Table 1**.

Figure 3

Volume of oxygen produced in 10 minutes (cm^3)

0 10 20 30 40 50 60 70

0 1 2 3 4 5 6 7 8 9 10

Relative light intensity

[2]

2.4 One of the student's results is anomalous.
At which relative light intensity is the result anomalous?

Relative light intensity = ...

[1]

2.5 Describe what the student's results show about the relationship between light intensity and rate of photosynthesis.

....

[1]

[Total 8 marks]

Respiration and Metabolism

1 Metabolism is the sum of all of the reactions that happen in a cell or the body. Metabolism includes reactions that make molecules. Grade 1-3

1.1 Complete the sentence below. Use a word from the box.

glycogen	**glycerol**	**amino acids**

Lipids are made from fatty acids and ....

[1]

1.2 What type of ion is needed to make amino acids?
Tick **one** box.

magnesium ☐ phosphate ☐ potassium ☐ nitrate ☐

[1]

1.3 Which of these molecules is **not** made during metabolism in animals?
Tick **one** box.

proteins ☐ glycogen ☐ cellulose ☐ lipids ☐

[1]

1.4 Metabolism also involves breaking down molecules.
What is produced when excess protein is broken down?

....

[1]

[Total 4 marks]

2 Respiration is an important chemical reaction. Grade 3-4

2.1 Complete the following sentences about respiration. Use words from the box.

exothermic	**from**	**endothermic**	**all**	**to**	**some**

Respiration is a reaction carried out by .... living organisms.

Respiration is an .... reaction.

It transfers energy .... the environment.

[3]

Figure 1 shows a gull.

Figure 1

2.2 Give **one** example of how a gull uses the energy transferred by respiration.

....

[1]

[Total 4 marks]

Target AO3

3 A student is investigating respiration in germinating peas. She predicts that germinating peas will respire, and so will release energy as heat.

The student sets up her experiment as shown in **Figure 2**.

Figure 2

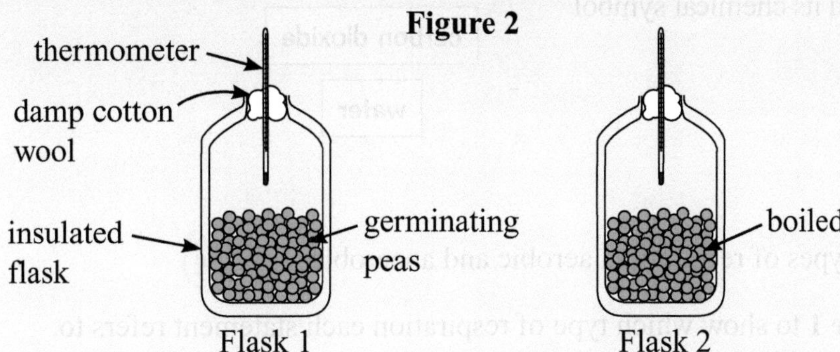

The student records the temperature of each flask at the beginning of the experiment (day 0), then every day for three days.

Table 1 shows her results.

Table 1

Day	Temperature (°C)	
	Flask 1	Flask 2
Day 0	20	20
Day 1	23	31
Day 2	25	21
Day 3	28	21

3.1 Give **one** variable that the student needed to control to make the experiment a fair test.

.... *[1]*

3.2 One of the student's readings was anomalous. Circle the anomalous reading in **Table 1**. *[1]*

3.3 Explain why the student included Flask 2 in her experiment.

....

.... *[1]*

3.4 Which of these statements is a conclusion the student can make based on her results?
Tick **one** box.

The temperature in both flasks decreased over time. ☐

The peas in Flask 1 released heat energy. ☐

Boiling the peas did not affect the amount of heat energy released. ☐

The peas in Flask 1 respired more on Day 3 than on Day 1. ☐

[1]

[Total 4 marks]

Exam Tip

When you're designing an experiment, or looking at a method in an exam, it's really important that only one thing is changed at a time. That way you can be sure it's the thing that's been changed that has affected the results.

Aerobic and Anaerobic Respiration

Warm-Up

Draw a line between each substance on the left and its chemical symbol on the right.

glucose	CO_2
carbon dioxide	H_2O
water	$C_6H_{12}O_6$

1 There are two types of respiration, aerobic and anaerobic. 

Complete **Table 1** to show which type of respiration each statement refers to.
Tick **one** box in each row.

Table 1

Statement	Aerobic respiration	Anaerobic respiration
It transfers more energy.		
It uses O_2.		
It can produce ethanol and CO_2 as products.		
It is the incomplete breakdown of glucose.		

[Total 3 marks]

2 An experiment was set up using a sealed beaker, with a carbon dioxide monitor attached. The set up is shown in **Figure 1**. 

Figure 1

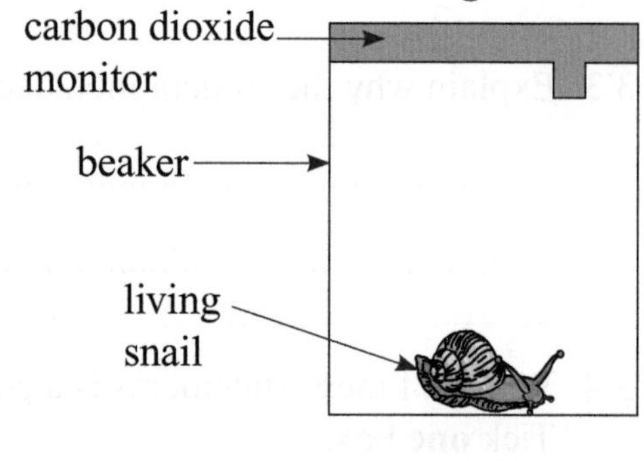

After two hours, the carbon dioxide concentration in the beaker in **Figure 1** had **increased**.

2.1 Explain why the carbon dioxide concentration in the beaker increased.

....

....

[1]

2.2 Suggest what happened to the level of **oxygen** in the beaker in **Figure 1** after two hours. Explain your answer.

....

....

[2]

[Total 3 marks]

Exam Tip

Whenever you see the word 'suggest' in an exam question, that's your cue to gather all your knowledge on that topic and apply it to a situation that you haven't seen before. So don't panic if you see an unfamiliar experiment or example — if the word 'suggest' is there, just take what you already know and use it to try to work out what might happen.

Exercise

1 Complete the sentences about exercise below.
Use words from the box.

lactic acid	**muscles**	**brain**	**glucose**	**oxygen**	**ethanol**

During exercise your .... may respire anaerobically.

This causes a build up of ....

It also leads to an .... debt.

[Total 3 marks]

2 A student was investigating the effect of exercise on his own breathing rate.
The results are shown in **Table 1**.

Grade 4-5

Table 1

	Breathing rate (number of breaths per minute)			
	Before exercise	During exercise	One minute after exercise	Five minutes after exercise
Repeat 1	11	16	15	12
Repeat 2	12	15	14	11
Repeat 3	11	15	14	12
Mean	11	15	14	

2.1 Calculate the mean breathing rate five minutes after exercise.

Mean = ... breaths per minute
[1]

2.2 Explain why the student's breathing rate increased during exercise.

....

....
[2]

2.3 Explain why the student's breathing rate remained high one minute after exercise.

....

....
[1]

2.4 Suggest what would have happened to the student's heart rate during the period of exercise.

....
[1]

[Total 5 marks]

Homeostasis

Warm-Up

The sentences below are about the control systems used in homeostasis.
Circle **one** underlined word or phrase in each sentence, so that the sentence is correct.

The control systems are/are not automatic.

If a control system detects the level of something is too high, it will increase/decrease the level.

If a control system detects the level of something is too low, it will increase/decrease the level.

1 Which of the following is **not** part of homeostasis? Tick **one** box. Grade 3-4

- responding to changes outside the body ☐
- keeping conditions inside the body at the right level ☐
- allowing large changes in conditions inside the body ☐
- responding to changes inside the body ☐

[Total 1 mark]

2 Human body temperature is kept at about 37 °C.
A homeostatic control system is used to do this. Grade 4-5

2.1 Suggest why it's important that body temperature is kept at around 37 °C.

....

[1]

2.2 A woman is exercising. As she exercises, her body temperature increases.
The following sentences outline how her body temperature will be brought back to normal.
Complete the sentences. Use words from the box.

a coordination centre	a stimulus	effectors	receptors

The increase in body temperature is detected by ....

Information is then sent to ....

The information is processed and a signal is sent to .... ,

which produce a response. The woman's body temperature decreases.

[3]

2.3 Shivering is a homeostatic response to a drop in body temperature. It is controlled by the nervous system. Which other system controls homeostatic responses?

....

[1]

[Total 5 marks]

The Nervous System

1 Information is carried through the nervous system as electrical impulses. Effectors react to these electrical impulses to produce a response. Grade 3-4

1.1 Which type of neurone carries electrical impulses to effectors?
Tick **one** box.

relay neurone ☐ motor neurone ☐ sensory neurone ☐

[1]

1.2 Muscles and glands are both types of effector. They respond differently to electrical impulses. How do muscles and glands respond to electrical impulses?

Muscles: ....

Glands: ....

[2]

[Total 3 marks]

2 **Figure 1** shows part of the human nervous system. Grade 4-5

Figure 1

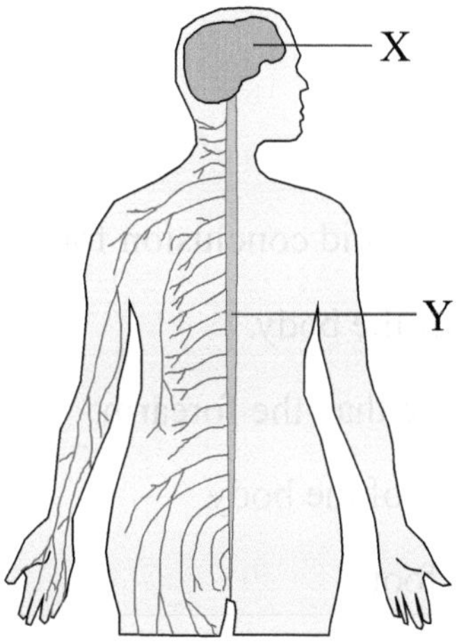

2.1 Name the structures labelled **X** and **Y** on **Figure 1**.

X ....

Y ....

[2]

2.2 Which part of the nervous system do structures **X** and **Y** form?

....

[1]

2.3 What is the role of the part of the nervous system formed by structures **X** and **Y**?

....

....

[1]

[Total 4 marks]

Target AO3

3 Two students are investigating the sensitivity of the skin on different areas of the body using the method below. 

1. Blindfold the person being tested.
2. Tape two toothpicks onto a ruler so that they are 50 mm apart.
3. Lightly press the two toothpicks onto the person's arm.
4. Ask whether the person can feel one or two toothpicks.
5. If they can feel two toothpicks, move the toothpicks 5 mm closer together and repeat steps 3 and 4. Keep doing this until they can only feel one toothpick.

The students did their experiment on different areas of the body and repeated it three times for each area. Each time, they recorded the distance between toothpicks at which the person could only feel one toothpick. Their results are shown in **Table 1**.

Table 1

Area of the body	Forearm			Palm			Back of hand		
Repeat	1	2	3	1	2	3	1	2	3
Distance between toothpicks (mm)	30	30	35	5	5	5	25	20	15

3.1 Calculate the mean distance between toothpicks for the back of the hand

Mean = ... mm

[2]

3.2 Which of the following sentences is a valid conclusion for this experiment? Tick **one** box.

The palm is the most sensitive part of the body. ☐

The back of the hand is more sensitive than the forearm. ☐

The forearm is the least sensitive part of the body. ☐

The palm is more sensitive than the foot. ☐

[1]

3.3 The cheek is less sensitive than the palm, but more sensitive than the back of the hand. Predict a possible value for the mean distance between toothpicks if the students tested the person's cheek.

.... mm

[1]

3.4 Another student repeated the experiment but she forgot to blindfold the person being tested. Suggest why this might have been a source of error.

....

....

[1]

[Total 5 marks]

Exam Tip

If you're asked to draw a conclusion from an experiment, don't go beyond what the data tells you. For example, in the experiment above, the students didn't test the feet — so you can't conclude anything about foot sensitivity from their data.

Synapses and Reflexes

Warm-Up

Which of these actions is a reflex?
Circle the correct answer.

Dropping a hot plate. | Writing a letter. | Running to catch a bus.

1 Which of the following sentences is correct? Tick **one** box. (Grade 3-4)

- Reflex reactions are slow and under conscious control. ☐
- Reflex reactions are slow and automatic. ☐
- Reflex reactions are rapid and automatic. ☐
- Reflex reactions are rapid and under conscious control. ☐

[Total 1 mark]

2 **Figure 1** shows a reflex arc. (Grade 4-5)

Figure 1

X Y A

2.1 Name structures **X** and **Y**.

X ....

Y ....

[2]

2.2 What is the **stimulus** shown in **Figure 1**?

....

[1]

2.3 Structure **A** is the junction between two neurones. Name structure **A**.

....

[1]

2.4 Explain how structure **Y** receives a signal about the stimulus.
Your answer should include how the signal is transmitted across structure **A**.

....

....

....

....

[4]

[Total 8 marks]

Exam Tip

If an exam question asks you to 'name' something like a structure or process, don't start writing an essay. In fact, you can stay clear of explaining or describing anything at all. A little word or phrase is all the examiners are looking for.

PRACTICAL

Investigating Reaction Time

1 A scientist carried out an experiment to investigate the impact of caffeine on reaction time.

- The scientist measured a volunteer's reaction time using a simple test.
- He then gave the volunteer a drink containing caffeine.
- After ten minutes, he measured the volunteer's reaction time again.
- He repeated the test on four different days with the same volunteer.

The results are shown in **Table 1**.

Table 1

	Reaction time (s)				
	Repeat 1	Repeat 2	Repeat 3	Repeat 4	Mean
Before caffeine	0.16	0.15	0.18	0.17	
After caffeine	0.13	0.14	0.16	0.14	0.15

1.1 Calculate the mean reaction time before the volunteer had caffeine.
Give your answer to two significant figures.

Mean = ... s

[2]

1.2 Which statement describes the results of the experiment? Tick **one** box.

Reaction time was slower after caffeine. ☐

Reaction time was faster after caffeine. ☐

Reaction time was no different after caffeine. ☐

[1]

1.3 Each time the scientist repeated the test he got similar results.
What does this say about the scientist's results? Tick **one** box.

The results are repeatable. ☐

There are no errors in the method. ☐

The results prove there's a link between caffeine and reaction time. ☐

[1]

1.4 Give **two** variables that the scientist should have kept the same each time he repeated the experiment.

1. ....

2. ....

[2]

[Total 6 marks]

Exam Tip

You'll definitely get tested on your practical knowledge as part of your exams. Make sure you know what terms like 'repeatable' and 'variable' mean, so you understand what questions like the ones above are asking you.

The Brain

Warm-Up

Which of these statements about the brain is true? Underline the correct answer.

The brain controls some of our complex behaviours.

The brain doesn't control our complex behaviours.

The brain controls all of our complex behaviours.

1 **Figure 1** shows the human brain. Labels **A**, **B** and **C** point to three different regions. 

1.1 Draw straight lines to match each letter below to the name of the brain region it represents in **Figure 1**.

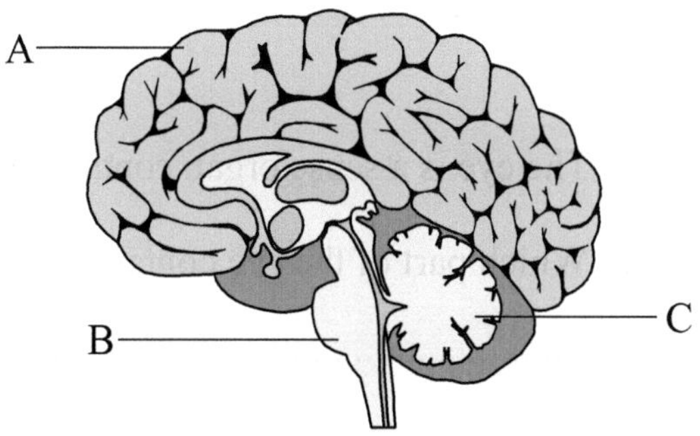

Letter	**Name of brain region**
A	spinal cord
B	cerebellum
C	cerebral cortex
	medulla

Figure 1

A

B

C

[3]

1.2 Name the type of cell that makes up most of the brain's material.

....

[1]

1.3 Give **one** function of the cerebral cortex.

....

[1]

1.4 Name the region of the brain that controls unconscious activities.

....

[1]

1.5 State **one** activity that takes place in the human body that is not under our conscious control.

....

[1]

[Total 7 marks]

The Eye

Warm-Up

Use the words below to correctly label the diagram of the eye.
Each word can only be used once.

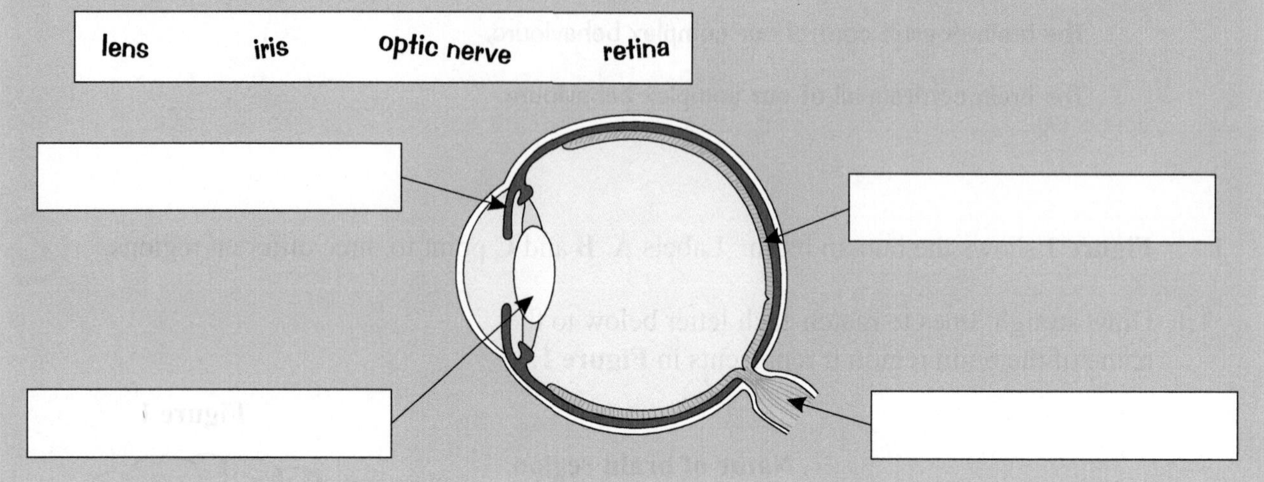

1 The eye is a sense organ containing receptors.

1.1 Which part of the eye contains receptor cells that detect light intensity and colour?

....

[1]

1.2 The optic nerve carries impulses away from the retina.
Where do the impulses go once they have left the retina? Tick **one** box.

☐ cornea ☐ brain ☐ sclera ☐ lens

[1]

1.3 Name the clear layer at the front of the eye.

....

[1]

1.4 Which part of the eye controls the size of the pupil?

....

[1]

1.5 Which **two** parts of the eye change the shape of the lens during focusing?

1. ....

2. ....

[2]

[Total 6 marks]

Exam Tip

If a multiple choice question tells you to 'tick one box', that tells you that only one of the options is right. If you don't know the answer, try crossing out the words by the boxes for any answers you know are not right, so you have fewer options to think about. And if you're still not certain, don't leave it blank — you might as well have an educated guess.

The Iris Reflex and Focusing

1 Accommodation is an action that happens in the eye. Grade 3-4

1.1 Which of the following statements about accommodation is **not** correct?
Tick **one** box.

It lets the eye focus on near objects. ☐

It changes the amount of light that enters the eye. ☐

It changes the shape of the lens. ☐

It is a reflex action. ☐

[1]

1.2 The following sentences outline how the accommodation reflex is used to focus on **distant** objects.
Use words from the box to complete the sentences.

tighten	**more**	**relax**	**thin**	**fat**	**less**

The ciliary muscles .... and the suspensory ligaments ....

This makes the lens go .... , so it refracts light ....

[4]

[Total 5 marks]

2 **Figure 1** shows a human eye as it would appear in two different light levels. Grade 4-5

Figure 1

A B

2.1 How does the size of the pupil in eye **A** in **Figure 1** differ from eye **B**?

....

....

[1]

2.2 Which eye, **A** or **B**, is in dim light? Explain your answer.

....

....

[1]

2.3 Give **one** reason why it is important for the size of the pupil to change in very bright light.

....

[1]

[Total 3 marks]

Correcting Vision Defects

1 Some people are short-sighted. Glasses can be worn to correct short-sightedness. Grade 4-5

1.1 What is the medical term for short-sightedness?

....

[1]

Figure 1 shows the eye of a person with short-sightedness.

Figure 1

distant object

1.2 Why will the person whose eye is shown in **Figure 1** not be able to see distant objects clearly?

....

....

[2]

Figure 2 shows how a lens (**X**) in glasses can be used to correct short-sightedness.

Figure 2

X

distant object

1.3 Explain how the lens (**X**) in **Figure 2** corrects the sight of a person with this vision defect.

....

....

....

[2]

1.4 A person has short-sightedness but finds wearing glasses uncomfortable.
Suggest **two** other ways that short-sightedness could be corrected.

1. ....

2. ....

[2]

[Total 7 marks]

Exam Tip

Ray diagrams of the eye (like the ones in Figures 1 and 2) can look a bit confusing, so take some time to get your head around them. They're just showing you how light enters the eye and how different types of lens can correct vision defects.

Controlling Body Temperature

1 The body responds differently to an increase or decrease in temperature. 

Complete **Table 1** to show whether each response happens when the body is too hot or too cold. Tick **one** box in each row.

Table 1

Response	Body is too hot	Body is too cold
Sweating		
Blood vessels constrict		
Shivering		

[Total 3 marks]

2 The body's thermoregulatory centre monitors and controls body temperature.

2.1 Name the organ of the body where the thermoregulatory centre is located.

....

[1]

2.2 The thermoregulatory centre contains receptors. What are these receptors sensitive to?

....

[1]

2.3 Briefly outline how the thermoregulatory centre receives information about the temperature outside the body.

....

....

....

[2]

[Total 4 marks]

3 If the body is too hot, blood vessels supplying the skin become wider.

3.1 What is the name of this process?

....

[1]

3.2 Explain how this process helps to return body temperature back to normal.

....

....

....

[2]

[Total 3 marks]

Exam Tip

Pay attention to how long you're spending on a question in the exam. If you take ages puzzling over a question you don't know the answer to, you might end up not having enough time for other questions that you could answer. If you're stuck, it's a good idea to move on. You can come back to the question at the end of the exam if you have time.

Target AO3

4 A scientist is using a model to investigate how sweating cools the body. 

The scientist fills two boiling tubes with hot water. She wraps one boiling tube with a wet paper towel and the other with a dry paper towel. She records the temperature of the water in each tube every minute. The results of the experiment are shown in **Table 2** and **Figure 1**.

Table 2

Time (min)	Dry (°C)	Wet (°C)
0	60	60
1	58	54
2	56	49
3	55	45
4	53	38
5	52	39
6	50	36
7	49	34
8	47	32
9	46	30
10	45	29

Figure 1

Temperature (°C)
60
50
40
30
0 1 2 3 4 5 6 7 8 9 10
Time (minutes)
dry
wet

4.1 Explain why the scientist ignored the result at 4 minutes when drawing the line of best fit for the **wet** paper towel in **Figure 1**.

....

[1]

4.2 The scientist said "The temperature decreased more rapidly in the tube wrapped in the wet paper towel than in the tube wrapped in the dry paper towel."

Say whether or not you agree with this statement. Use data from **Table 2** to support your answer.

....

....

....

[3]

4.3 Give **one** variable that the scientist should have controlled during the experiment.

....

[1]

4.4 Identify the dependent variable in the scientist's experiment.

....

[1]

[Total 6 marks]

Exam Tip

When you're given a graph to look at in an exam, make sure that you've read the scales and any labels carefully before you start writing. If you've done that, you can be sure that you have a good grasp of what the lines are telling you.

The Endocrine System

1 Figure 1 shows the positions of some glands in the human body. Grade 1-3

Figure 1

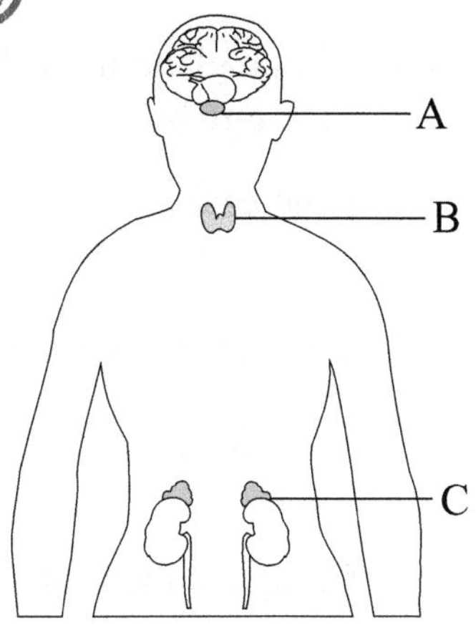

Which part of the diagram, **A**, **B** or **C**, represents the thyroid gland?

Your answer = ...

[Total 1 mark]

2 The endocrine system is a collection of glands in the body that secrete hormones. Grade 3-4

2.1 Which of the following statements about glands is correct?
Tick **one** box.

Glands secrete hormones directly into cells. ☐

Glands secrete hormones directly into the blood. ☐

Glands secrete hormones directly into organs. ☐

[1]

2.2 Which of the following statements best describes hormones?
Tick **one** box.

Hormones are cells. ☐ Hormones are chemicals. ☐ Hormones are enzymes. ☐

[1]

2.3 State **two** ways in which the effects of the endocrine system differ from the nervous system.

1. ....

2. ....

[2]

[Total 4 marks]

3 One of the glands in the body is known as the 'master gland'.
This gland secretes several hormones in response to body conditions. Grade 4-5

3.1 What is the name of the 'master gland'?

....

[1]

3.2 What is the function of the hormones released by the 'master gland'?

....

....

[2]

[Total 3 marks]

Controlling Blood Glucose

1 The concentration of glucose in the blood is controlled by hormones. Grade 3-4

1.1 Which gland in the human body monitors and controls blood glucose concentration?
Tick **one** box.

pancreas ☐ pituitary gland ☐ thyroid ☐ testis ☐

[1]

1.2 Which hormone is produced when blood glucose concentration becomes too high?

....

[1]

1.3 Complete the sentences to describe what happens when there is too much glucose in the blood.
Use words from the box.

pancreas	**glycogen**	**insulin**	**liver**

When there is too much glucose in the blood, some of it moves into the ....

The glucose is then changed into .... so it can be stored.

[2]

[Total 4 marks]

2 Diabetes exists in two different forms, Type 1 and Type 2. Grade 4-5

2.1 Which of the following statements describes **Type 1** diabetes?
Tick **one** box.

The body produces too little glucose. ☐

The body becomes resistant to its own insulin. ☐

The body produces too much insulin. ☐

The body produces little or no insulin. ☐

[1]

2.2 How is **Type 1** diabetes treated?

....

[1]

2.3 Give **two** treatments that a doctor would recommend for **Type 2** diabetes.

1. ....

2. ....

[2]

2.4 Give a risk factor for **Type 2** diabetes.

....

[1]

[Total 5 marks]

The Kidneys

1 Unwanted substances are removed from the body in the urine. Grade 4-5

1.1 What is the name of the process by which the kidneys produce urine?
Tick **one** box.

active transport ☐ filtration ☐ osmosis ☐ diffusion ☐

[1]

1.2 Name **one** unwanted substance that is removed from the kidneys in urine.

....

[1]

A process in the kidneys returns useful substances to the blood so that they are not lost in urine.

1.3 What is the name of this process?

....

[1]

1.4 Name **two** useful substances that are returned to the blood by this process.

1. ....

2. ....

[2]

[Total 5 marks]

2 Some water leaves the body in the urine. Water can also be lost from the skin by sweating. Grade 4-5

2.1 Give **one** other way that water can be lost from the body.

....

[1]

2.2 Name **one** substance other than water that is lost through the skin in sweat.

....

[1]

2.3 Which of the following statements is true?
Tick **one** box.

The body can control water loss from the skin. ☐

The body can only control water loss from the skin at night. ☐

The body can't control water loss from the skin. ☐

[1]

2.4 Why can cells be damaged if the body's water balance is wrong?

....

....

[1]

[Total 4 marks]

Kidney Failure

Warm-Up

Draw circles to show whether the statements below are **true** or **false**.

Kidney transplants are a cure for kidney failure.	True / False
Dialysis only has to be done once.	True / False
Transplants involve major surgery.	True / False

1 **Figure 1** shows the operation of a dialysis machine. Grade 4-5

Figure 1

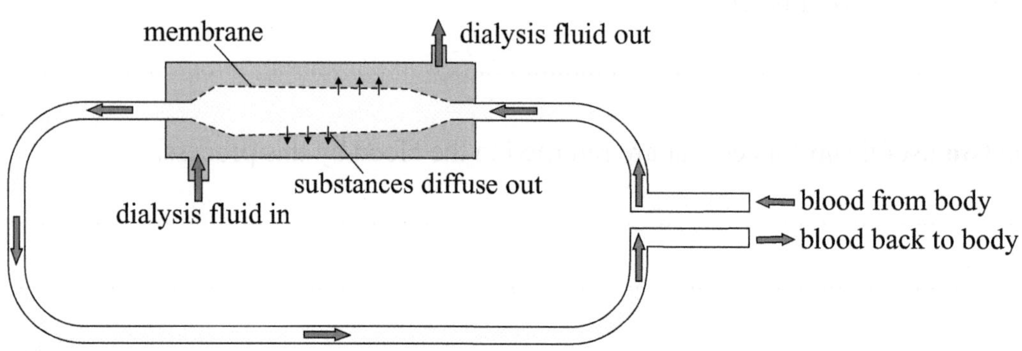

1.1 What type of membrane does a dialysis machine have? Tick **one** box.

partially permeable ☐ fully permeable ☐ non permeable ☐

[1]

1.2 A person's blood flows through the dialysis machine.
Complete the sentences to describe what happens during dialysis. Use words from the box.

the same	a different	waste	useful	glucose	urea

Healthy blood and dialysis fluid have .... concentration of ions.

.... substances are not lost from the blood during dialysis.

.... substances diffuse across the membrane and out of the patient's blood.

.... is an example of a substance that leaves the patient's blood.

[4]

1.3 Give **one** disadvantage of using dialysis to treat kidney failure.

....

....

[1]

[Total 6 marks]

Exam Tip

If you're given a tricky-looking diagram in the exam, don't be thrown by it. Chances are it might be similar to one you've met before, but just drawn a bit differently. And even if it is about something new, everything that you need to help you understand it will be there somewhere. Look carefully at any arrows or labels and read all the information you're given.

Puberty and the Menstrual Cycle

1 Males begin producing sex hormones during puberty. Grade 1-3

1.1 What is the main sex hormone in men? Tick **one** box.

insulin ☐ testosterone ☐ oestrogen ☐ adrenaline ☐

[1]

1.2 Where is the main sex hormone in men produced? Tick **one** box.

pancreas ☐ pituitary gland ☐ thyroid gland ☐ testes ☐

[1]

1.3 Which of the following is a role of the main sex hormone in men? Tick **one** box.

stimulating egg production ☐ control of water content in the body ☐

control of blood glucose levels ☐ stimulating sperm production ☐

[1]

[Total 3 marks]

2 Female sex hormones control the menstrual cycle. Grade 3-4

2.1 What is the name of the main female reproductive hormone produced in the ovary?

....

[1]

2.2 What is the name of the process by which eggs are released from the ovary?

....

[1]

2.3 How often is an egg released from an ovary? Tick **one** box.

Every 7 days. ☐ Every 14 days. ☐ Every 21 days. ☐ Every 28 days. ☐

[1]

2.4 Name the hormone that causes the release of an egg.

....

[1]

[Total 4 marks]

3 During the menstrual cycle, a change in the level of progesterone causes the woman to menstruate (bleed). Grade 4-5

Suggest how the progesterone level changes before a woman starts to bleed. Explain your answer.

....

....

....

....

[Total 3 marks]

Controlling Fertility

Warm-Up

All of the methods below are forms of contraception. Circle the **two** hormonal methods.

avoiding sexual intercourse   condom   contraceptive injection   contraceptive patch   diaphragm

1 Some methods of contraception use hormones to control the fertility of a woman. Grade 4-5

1.1 How is an oral contraceptive taken into the body?
Tick **one** box.

As an injection. ☐

As a tablet taken by mouth. ☐

Through the skin from a patch. ☐

[1]

1.2 How do oral contraceptives containing multiple hormones prevent pregnancy?
Tick **one** box.

The hormones stop oestrogen production. ☐

The hormones stop FSH production. ☐

The hormones stop LH production. ☐

[1]

1.3 The contraceptive implant is inserted under the skin of the arm.
Which hormone does it release?

....

[1]

1.4 How does the hormone released by the contraceptive implant prevent pregnancy?

....

[1]

1.5 An oral contraceptive has to be taken daily.
Suggest **one** advantage of the contraceptive implant over an oral contraceptive.
Explain your answer.

....

....

[2]

[Total 6 marks]

Exam Tip

Knowing the roles of the hormones that control the menstrual cycle can be very handy when it comes to understanding how those hormones are used in contraceptives. So make sure you've got them all sorted out in your head.

More on Controlling Fertility

Warm-Up

Draw lines to match the barrier method of contraception on the left, to the description of how it's worn on the right.

Method of contraception	Description
diaphragm	worn inside the vagina
male condom	worn over the entrance to the uterus
female condom	worn over the penis

1 There are several different non-hormonal methods of contraception. These include barrier methods of contraception.

Grade 4-5

1.1 How do barrier methods of contraception prevent a woman from becoming pregnant?
Tick **one** box.

They break down eggs once they have been fertilised by sperm. ☐

They prevent eggs from being released. ☐

They stop sperm from getting to an egg. ☐

They kill sperm. ☐

[1]

1.2 Name a barrier method of contraception that protects against sexually transmitted infections.

....

[1]

1.3 Some barrier methods need to be used with spermicides.
Explain how spermicides help to prevent pregnancy.

....

....

....

[2]

1.4 A couple not wishing to have children do not want to use any form of contraception.
Suggest how they could avoid pregnancy.

....

....

[1]

[Total 5 marks]

Exam Tip

Remember to read all the different options in multiple choice questions. Don't be tempted to dive right in and tick the first option that sounds right — sometimes there might only be slight differences in the wording of different options.

Plant Hormones

1 Auxin controls plant growth in response to different stimuli. Grade 1-3

1.1 Which of the following statements about auxin is true?
Tick **one** box.

Auxin causes plant cells in shoots to get longer. ☐

Auxin causes plant cells in roots to get longer. ☐

Auxin causes plant cells in shoots to stop getting longer. ☐

[1]

1.2 Which of the following answers should be used to complete the sentence?
Write the correct letter, **A**, **B** or **C**, in the box below.

A light

B gravity

C water

Geotropism is the growth of a plant in response to ☐.

[1]

[Total 2 marks]

PRACTICAL

2 A student carried out an experiment to investigate the effect of light on plant growth. Grade 4-5

- The student grew two sets of cress seedlings.
- **Set A** received light from all sides.
- **Set B** were placed in a box with a slit in one side. They received light from one side only.
- The results are shown in **Figure 1**.

Figure 1

2.1 Compare the growth of the seedlings in **Set A** with those in **Set B**.

....

....

[2]

2.2 What name is given to the response shown by the shoots in **Set B**?
Tick **one** box.

phototropism ☐ gravitropism ☐ germination ☐

[1]

2.3 The experiment was repeated. The seedlings in **Set B** were placed in the same box. The box was placed the other way round so the seedlings received light from the left instead. Suggest how the results might be different from those shown in **Figure 1**.

....

....

[1]

2.4 Give **one** example of a variable that should be controlled in the experiment.

....

[1]

[Total 5 marks]

Target AO3

3 A student is investigating how the tip of a plant shoot affects its growth.

He sets up three groups of seedlings (**Groups A-C**), as shown in **Figure 2**.

Figure 2

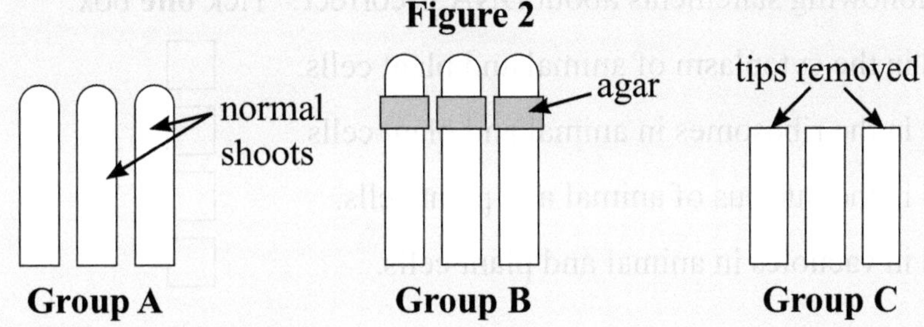

The tips of the shoots in **Group B** were cut off and a piece of agar was placed between the tip and the rest of the shoot. Agar lets water-soluble substances such as auxin pass through it. The tips of the shoots in **Group C** were cut off and nothing was added.

After one week, all of the shoots in **Groups A and B** had grown, while the shoots in **Group C** had not grown.

3.1 Explain the purpose of **Group C** in the experiment.

....

....

[1]

3.2 Suggest an explanation for the results that the student saw in **Group B**.

....

....

[1]

3.3 Describe how the student could show that his results are **repeatable**.

....

....

[1]

3.4 The student designs another experiment to test if it is auxin that is causing the shoots to grow. Complete the sentences to describe the method for this experiment. Use words from the box.

roots	hour	tips	cut shoots	agar	week

1. Cut the .... off a group of seedlings.
2. Soak pieces of .... in a solution of auxin.
3. Place the soaked pieces on top of the ....
4. Leave the seedlings for one ....

[4]

[Total 7 marks]

Exam Tip

Figuring out what's going on in an experiment you're not familiar with can be pretty tricky. Make sure you read all of the information that the question gives you carefully — try underlining the key words to help you make sense of it.

DNA

1 DNA makes up the genetic material in animal and plant cells. Grade 3-4

1.1 Which of the following statements about DNA is correct? Tick **one** box.

- [ ] DNA is found in the cytoplasm of animal and plant cells.
- [ ] DNA is found in the ribosomes in animal and plant cells.
- [ ] DNA is found in the nucleus of animal and plant cells.
- [ ] DNA is found in vacuoles in animal and plant cells.

[1]

1.2 What are chromosomes? Tick **one** box.

- [ ] Proteins coded for by DNA.
- [ ] The structures that contain DNA.
- [ ] The site of protein synthesis.
- [ ] The bases that make up DNA.

[1]

[Total 2 marks]

2 **Figure 1** shows part of a DNA molecule. Grade 4-5

Figure 1

2.1 Describe the overall structure of a DNA molecule.

....

....

[2]

2.2 DNA contains lots of sections called genes. Describe the function of genes.

....

....

[2]

2.3 What is meant by the term genome?

....

....

[1]

2.4 Give **one** reason why it is important for scientists to understand the human genome.

....

....

[1]

[Total 6 marks]

Exam Tip

To properly understand this topic, you need to know how DNA, genes, chromosomes, proteins and amino acids relate to each other. Once you've got all of that sorted out, it'll make answering the questions a whole lot easier.

The Structure of DNA

Warm-Up

Draw a line from the sentence on the left to the correct ending of the sentence on the right.

A polymer is...

...made up of lots of smaller, repeating units.

...a smaller, repeating unit that makes up a larger structure.

1 A DNA nucleotide contains one of four bases. Grade 4-5

1.1 What are the four bases found in DNA?
Tick **one** box.

- A, T, P and G ☐
- C, T, G and F ☐
- A, C, G and T ☐
- T, C, A and E ☐

[1]

Figure 1 shows a DNA nucleotide.

Figure 1

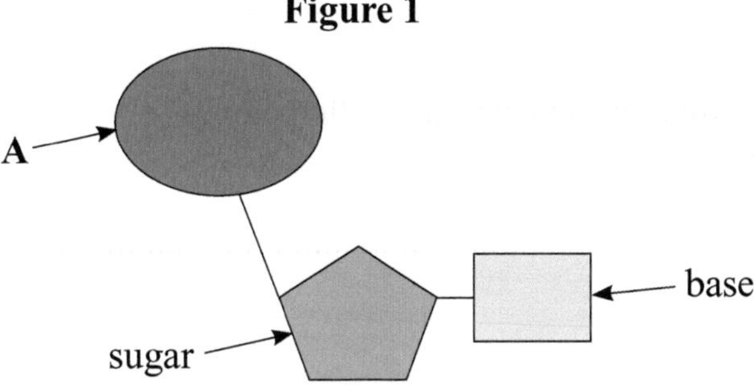

1.2 Name the part labelled **A**.

....

[1]

1.3 How many bases are needed to code for one specific amino acid?

....

[1]

1.4 The order of bases in DNA can affect which protein is made. Explain why.

....

....

....

[2]

[Total 5 marks]

Reproduction

1 Sexual reproduction involves male and female gametes. 

Draw **one** line from each type of gamete on the left to the correct description on the right.

Type of gamete	Description
sperm	female gamete
egg	male gamete in animals
pollen	male gamete in plants

[Total 2 marks]

2 There are different types of cell division in sexual and asexual reproduction.

2.1 Which type of cell division is involved in the production of gametes?

....

[1]

2.2 Name the type of cell division used in asexual reproduction.

....

[1]

2.3 Cells produced by asexual reproduction are called clones.
What does this mean?

....

[1]

[Total 3 marks]

3 There are several differences between asexual and sexual reproduction.

Complete **Table 1** to show if each statement applies to asexual or sexual reproduction.
Tick **one** box in each row.

Table 1

	Asexual reproduction	Sexual reproduction
There is only one parent.		
There is no mixing of genes.		
It results in genetic variation in the offspring.		
There is fusion of gametes.		

[Total 3 marks]

Meiosis

1 Sexual reproduction in humans involves meiosis. (Grade 4-5)

1.1 Where in the body does meiosis take place? Tick **one** box.

all tissues ☐

growing tissues only ☐

the skin ☐

the reproductive organs ☐

[1]

1.2 Before a cell starts to divide by meiosis, what happens to its DNA?

....

[1]

1.3 How many cell divisions are there during the process of meiosis?

....

[1]

1.4 Briefly describe the results of meiosis.

....

....

....

....

[3]

[Total 6 marks]

2 After an egg cell has been fertilised, it divides many times. (Grade 4-5)

2.1 What type of cell division does the fertilised egg cell undergo?

....

[1]

2.2 The dividing cells form an embryo.
What happens to the cells in the embryo as it develops in order to form the whole organism?

....

....

[1]

[Total 2 marks]

Exam Tip

It's easy to get mixed up between meiosis and mitosis. Remember, meiosis is the one that makes eggs and sperm. Mitosis makes twin (identical) cells. Even if you know the difference, it's still easy to accidentally write one when you mean the other, just because the words are so similar. So always check your answer through after you've written it.

More on Reproduction

Warm-Up

Complete the passage using words from below. You don't need to use every word.

runners different spores stalks identical seeds

Some organisms can reproduce both sexually and asexually. For example, strawberry plants reproduce asexually using .... and reproduce sexually by producing ....
Asexual reproduction in strawberry plants results in genetically .... offspring, whereas sexual reproduction produces genetically .... offspring.

1 Some organisms can reproduce both sexually and asexually. (Grade 4-5)

1.1 Some plants and the malaria parasite can reproduce both sexually and asexually.
Give **one** other example of a type of organism that can reproduce both sexually and asexually.

....

[1]

1.2 Daffodils can reproduce by producing seeds or bulbs. Bulbs divide to form new plants.
What type of reproduction is shown when the bulbs divide to produce new plants?

....

[1]

1.3 Which of these statements about the reproduction of the malaria parasite is true? Tick **one** box.

- ☐ Malaria parasites reproduce sexually in the human host, but asexually in the mosquito.
- ☐ Malaria parasites reproduce sexually in both the human host and the mosquito.
- ☐ Malaria parasites reproduce asexually in the human host, but sexually in the mosquito.
- ☐ Malaria parasites reproduce asexually in both the human host and the mosquito.

[1]

1.4 A change in the environment can affect the survival of organisms.
Which of these statements about the benefits of sexual reproduction is true? Tick **one** box.

- ☐ It's faster than asexual reproduction, so organisms can produce more offspring. This increases the chance that some of the offspring will survive in the new environment.
- ☐ It creates variation in the offspring. This means it's more likely that some offspring will have characteristics that make them better able to survive in the new environment.
- ☐ It reduces variation in the offspring. This means it's less likely that some offspring will have characteristics that make them unable to survive in the environment.

[1]

[Total 4 marks]

X and Y Chromosomes

1 Chromosomes help to determine the characteristics of individuals, including their sex. Grade 1-3

1.1 How many pairs of chromosomes are there in a normal human body cell?
Tick **one** box.

22 ☐ 23 ☐ 24 ☐ 25 ☐

[1]

1.2 How many pairs of chromosomes decide what sex you are?
Tick **one** box.

1 ☐ 2 ☐ 4 ☐ 8 ☐

[1]
[Total 2 marks]

2 **Figure 1** is an incomplete genetic diagram.
It shows how the sex chromosomes are inherited in humans. Grade 4-5

Figure 1

Sex chromosomes of parents: XX, XY

Gametes: X

Offspring: XY

2.1 Circle the male parent in **Figure 1**.

[1]

2.2 Fill in the sex chromosomes of the gametes produced by each parent in **Figure 1**.

[1]

2.3 Complete **Figure 1** to show the combination of sex chromosomes in the offspring.

[1]

2.4 What is the ratio of male to female offspring in the cross in **Figure 1**?

....

[1]
[Total 4 marks]

Exam Tip

You could be asked to complete a genetic diagram in the exam. Most of the time they deal with how individual genes are passed on, but here you're dealing with whole chromosomes. Don't forget that genetic diagrams can be drawn in a few different ways — you might also see them drawn in the form of a Punnett square or a family tree.

Genetic Diagrams

Warm-Up

Use the words and phrases to complete the passage below. You don't have to use every one.

homozygous   alleles   multiple genes   dominant

Genes exist in different versions called ....

If the two versions are the same, the organism is .... for that gene.

Some characteristics are controlled by a single gene, but most are controlled by

....

1 Hair length in dogs is controlled by two alleles. Short hair is caused by the dominant allele, 'H'. Long hair is caused by the recessive allele, 'h'. Grade 3-4

Figure 1 shows a genetic diagram of a cross between a short-haired and a long-haired dog. The offspring's genotypes are not shown.

Figure 1

parents' genotypes: HH   hh

gametes' genotypes: H   H   h   h

offspring's genotypes: ◯ ◯ ◯ ◯

1.1 Circle the long-haired parent in **Figure 1**.

[1]

1.2 All the offspring have the same genotype.
What is the offspring's genotype? Tick **one** box.

Hh ☐   HH ☐   h ☐   hh ☐

[1]

1.3 What phenotype do the offspring have?

....

[1]

[Total 3 marks]

Exam Tip

Watch out for those upper and lower case letters in genetic diagrams. It's very easy to write 'H' when you mean 'h'. Getting just one letter wrong in the gametes could mess up the genotypes of the offspring, so be really careful.

Inherited Disorders

1 Polydactyly is an inherited disorder. Grade 1-3

1.1 What are the symptoms of polydactyly?
Tick **one** box.

missing fingers or toes ☐

faulty cell membranes ☐

extra fingers or toes ☐

[1]

1.2 Which of the following statements about polydactyly is correct?
Tick **one** box.

It is caused by a recessive allele. ☐

It is caused by a dominant allele. ☐

It is only inherited by boys. ☐

Two copies of the allele are needed for an individual to have polydactyly. ☐

[1]

[Total 2 marks]

2 Cystic fibrosis is an inherited disorder.
The allele which causes cystic fibrosis is a recessive allele, 'f'.
'F' represents the dominant allele. Grade 4-5

Figure 1 is an incomplete Punnett square.
It shows the possible inheritance of cystic fibrosis from one couple.

Figure 1

	○	○
F	FF	Ff
F	FF	

2.1 Complete the Punnett square to show:
- the missing gametes' genotypes,
- the missing offspring's genotype.

[2]

2.2 What proportion of the possible offspring are heterozygous?

....

[1]

2.3 What proportion of the possible offspring have cystic fibrosis?

....

[1]

[Total 4 marks]

Family Trees and Embryo Screening

1 **Figure 1** shows a family tree. The family have a history of an inherited disorder. 

Figure 1

Freddy Zelda

Arthur Akheira Hilda Buster

Key
Male Female
Have the disorder
Carrier of the disorder but unaffected
Unaffected and not a carrier

1.1 Which family member is **not** a carrier of the disorder? Tick **one** box.

Hilda ☐ Freddy ☐ Zelda ☐ Buster ☐

[1]

The disorder is caused by a recessive allele, 'd'. The dominant allele is 'D'.

1.2 What is **Arthur's** genotype? Tick **one** box.

DD ☐ Dd ☐ dd ☐ d ☐

[1]

1.3 What is **Zelda's** genotype?

....

[1]

[Total 3 marks]

2 Embryos can be screened for genetic disorders like cystic fibrosis.
The results of screening sometimes results in the embryo being destroyed.
There are lots of arguments for and against embryo screening.

Grade 4-5

2.1 Give **one** argument **against** embryo screening.

....

....

[1]

2.2 Give **one** argument **for** embryo screening.

....

....

[1]

[Total 2 marks]

Exam Tip

Family trees can be confusing, but don't panic. Look at the key first, to make sure you understand what each symbol means. It can also be helpful to write the genotypes of the family members next to their symbols as you work them out. This will make it easier to keep track of whose genotypes you already know, and whose you still need to work out.

The Work of Mendel

Warm-Up

Circle the correct words or phrases below so that the passage is correct.

Gregor Mendel was an Austrian monk. He is best known for his work on speciation/evolution/genetics. In the late 18th/early 19th/mid 19th century he performed many breeding experiments using fungi/plants/pigs.

1 Scientists did not realise the importance of Gregor Mendel's research until after his death.

1.1 During his experiments, Mendel made several observations. Which of these statements was one of Mendel's observations? Tick **one** box.

- [ ] Pea plants grow to different heights randomly.
- [ ] Individuals within a species will not show any variation.
- [ ] Changes that occur in an organism during its life can be passed on.
- [ ] Units of inheritance are passed on to offspring unchanged.

[1]

1.2 Why did scientists at the time not understand how important Mendel's work was? Tick **one** box.

- [ ] His experiments were not carried out as fair tests.
- [ ] They did not have the background knowledge to fully understand his work.
- [ ] There was other evidence that contradicted Mendel's work.
- [ ] Mendel's work was not published until after his death.

[1]

1.3 In the early 20th century, scientists discovered something that behaved in a similar way to Mendel's 'hereditary units'. What was it that scientists discovered?

....

[1]

[Total 3 marks]

Exam Tip

You need to know about several important scientists and their work. It's important that you're confident that you know what each of these scientists is best known for — it could be easy to get them mixed up. Make sure you take some time now to get them straight in your head. You'll thank yourself if you get a question on one of them in your exam.

Variation

1 Mutations can lead to variation in an organism. (Grade 1-3)

1.1 What is a mutation?

....

[1]

1.2 Which of the following answers should be used to complete the sentence?
Write **A**, **B** or **C** in the box below.

A Most

B Very few

C All

☐ mutations have a large effect on the phenotype of an organism.

[1]

[Total 2 marks]

2 **Figure 1** shows two plants of different species, **A** and **B**.
Both plants were grown in the same controlled environmental conditions in a greenhouse. (Grade 3-4)

Figure 1

A **B**

Give **one** example of a difference between plants **A** and **B** which is likely to be due to genetic variation.

....

[Total 1 mark]

3 Kala and Leilani are identical twins. This means they have identical DNA. (Grade 4-5)

Kala weighs 7 kg more than Leilani.
Explain whether this is due to genes, environmental factors or both.

....

....

[Total 2 marks]

Exam Tip

Remember, variation can be caused by genes, environmental factors, or a mixture of both. In the exam, you might get asked about an example of variation that you've never heard of before. Don't worry if you do — all the information that you need in order to answer the question will be there. Just read it all through carefully and then apply your knowledge.

Evolution

Warm-Up

Put a tick (✓) in the box next to the correct name of the book published by Darwin in 1859.

On the Origin of Species ☐ On the Progression of Organisms ☐

1 Complete the sentences about evolution below. Use words from the box. Grade 3-4

environmental	three	inherited	some	all	six

Evolution is a change in the .... characteristics of a population over time. According to the theory of evolution by natural selection, ... organisms evolved from simple life forms that first started to develop over .... billion years ago.

[Total 3 marks]

2 Over time, many species have become extinct. Grade 3-4

2.1 What does it mean if a species becomes extinct?

....

[1]

2.2 Give **two** factors which might cause a species to become extinct.

1. ....

2. ....

[2]

[Total 3 marks]

3 Evolution by natural selection can sometimes result in the formation of two new species with very different phenotypes. Grade 4-5

3.1 What is the name of the process by which new species form?

....

[1]

3.2 Explain how you could know for certain if two populations of one original species had become two new species.

....

....

[1]

[Total 2 marks]

4 Charles Darwin proposed the theory of evolution by natural selection. Grade 4-5

4.1 Some of the evidence for his theory came from his round-the-world trip.
What other sources of developing knowledge helped Darwin to come up with his theory?
Tick **two** boxes.

fossils ☐ mutations ☐ bacteria ☐ geology ☐

[2]

4.2 When Darwin proposed his theory, he wasn't able to explain how characteristics are passed on.
What explanation has since been found for how characteristics are passed on?

....

....

[1]

4.3 Other theories on evolution existed at the same time as Darwin's.
One of these was suggested by Jean-Baptise Lamarck.
What did Lamarck believe about the method of evolution? Tick **one** box.

Changes that happen during an organism's lifetime are passed on to its offspring. ☐

Organisms that are not suited to their environment are more likely to reproduce. ☐

Changes that happen during an organism's lifetime are not passed on to its offspring. ☐

[1]

[Total 4 marks]

5* **Figure 1** is a photograph of a hare species which lives in a warm climate. It has large ears which help to keep it cool. The size of ears in hares is partly controlled by genes. Grade 4-5

Figure 1

Describe how natural selection could have led to the evolution of hares with large ears, from a population of hares with smaller ears.

....

....

....

....

....

....

....

....

....

....

[Total 6 marks]

Exam Tip

The process of how evolution occurs through natural selection always follows the same steps. If you learn these steps, then you should be able to apply them to explain any example of evolution that you're asked about in the exam.

Selective Breeding

1 Selective breeding is used in several different industries. (Grade 3-4)

1.1 What is selective breeding?

....
[1]

1.2 Which of these is another name for the process of selective breeding? Tick **one** box.

evolution ☐ natural selection ☐ inheritance ☐ artificial selection ☐

[1]

Figure 1 shows four wheat plants (**A-D**). Each plant has different characteristics.

Figure 1

head

stem

A ☐ **B** ☐ **C** ☐ **D** ☐

1.3 Which two plants should be bred together to get a wheat plant with a tall stem and a large head? Tick **two** boxes.

[1]

1.4 Suggest why dairy farmers might use selective breeding.

....
[1]

[Total 4 marks]

2 Selectively breeding organisms can lead to inbreeding. (Grade 4-5)

2.1 Inbreeding can make a population more likely to get a disease. Explain why.

....

....
[2]

2.2 Describe **one** other problem which may be caused by inbreeding.

....
[1]

[Total 3 marks]

Exam Tip

Selective breeding is another one of those processes that examiners like to get you to apply your knowledge to. Whatever feature you're asked about, the key thing to remember is this: you select the offspring with the best of that feature and breed them together. It doesn't matter what the feature in the question is — it's always the same process.

Genetic Engineering

1 Genetic engineering has many uses. Grade 1-3

1.1 What is genetic engineering? Tick **one** box.

Choosing organisms with particular characteristics to produce the next generation. ☐

The transfer of a gene from one organism's DNA into another organism's DNA. ☐

Creating the right conditions for the growth of organisms. ☐

[1]

1.2 How can bacteria be genetically engineered to help someone with diabetes? Tick **one** box.

They can be made to produce antibiotics. ☐

They can be made to produce antibodies. ☐

They can be made to produce insulin. ☐

[1]

[Total 2 marks]

2 Crop plants can be genetically engineered to be resistant to herbicides. Grade 3-4

2.1 What is the benefit of genetically engineering crop plants to be resistant to herbicides? Tick **one** box.

It makes the crop healthier. ☐

It makes the crop cheaper to grow. ☐

It can increase crop yield. ☐

It reduces damage to the crop from pests. ☐

[1]

2.2 Give **two** other ways in which crop plants are genetically engineered.

1. ....

2. ....

[2]

[Total 3 marks]

3 A team of scientists is investigating the number of wildflowers in two meadows. One meadow is next to a field containing a GM crop. The other meadow is next to a field containing a non-GM crop. The scientists compare their results for the two meadows. Grade 4-5

3.1 Suggest why the scientists are carrying out this investigation.

....

....

[1]

3.2 Suggest **one** thing the scientists could do to make their results more valid.

....

[1]

[Total 2 marks]

Cloning

Warm-Up

What is **cloning**? Underline the correct answer.

Producing genetically identical copies of plants and animals.

Producing genetically different copies of plants and animals.

Changing the DNA of a plant or animal.

1 Complete the sentences about cloning below. Use words from the box. 

plant	**sperm cell**	**animal**	**nucleus**

Adult cell cloning is used to make .... clones.

A .... is put into an empty egg cell.

[Total 2 marks]

2 There are several differences between embryo transplants and adult cell cloning. 

Complete **Table 1** to show which type of cloning each statement refers to.
Tick **one** box in each row.

Table 1

Statement	Embryo transplants	Adult cell cloning
The nucleus is removed from an unfertilised egg.		
The egg cell is given an electric shock.		
Cells are split apart before they become specialised.		
Several cloned embryos are formed.		
The nucleus is removed from an adult body cell.		

[Total 3 marks]

3 Plants can be cloned by tissue culture or by taking cuttings. 

3.1 Which of the following statements is correct?
Tick **one** box.

- Taking cuttings is an older and simpler method than tissue culture. ☐
- Tissue culture is a newer and simpler method than taking cuttings. ☐
- Taking cuttings is a newer and more complicated method than tissue culture. ☐
- Tissue culture is an older and more complicated method than taking cuttings. ☐

[1]

Figure 1 shows the process of tissue culture.

Figure 1

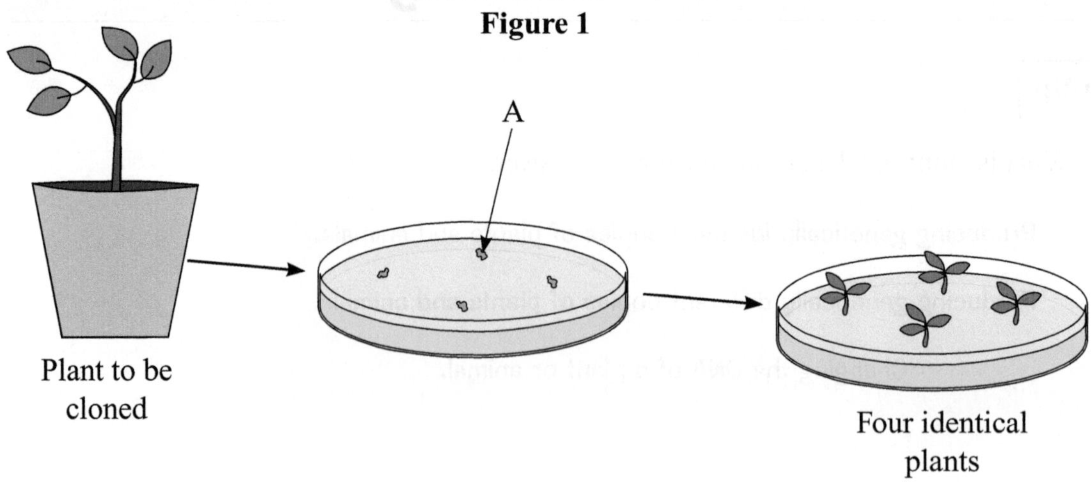

3.2 What is in the Petri dish in **Figure 1**, labelled A?

....

[1]

3.3 Give **one** use of plant tissue culture.

....

....

[1]

[Total 3 marks]

4* Describe how animal clones can be made using embryo transplants. Grade 4-5

....

....

....

....

....

....

....

....

....

[Total 4 marks]

Exam Tip

Make sure you've got the two different types of animal cloning that you need to know about (adult cell cloning and embryo transplants) clear in your head. Try writing down all of the steps for both methods. Check what you've written, then write them out again if you missed anything. Keep doing this until you know every step for both methods.

Fossils

Warm-Up

Draw circles to show whether the statements below are **true** or **false**.

Fossils are all between 100 and 1000 years old. True / False

Fossils are the remains of organisms. True / False

Fossils are often found in rocks. True / False

1 Scientists are not sure how life on Earth began.

Which of the following answers should be used to complete the sentence?
Write the correct letter, **A**, **B** or **C**, in the box below.

A there weren't the right conditions for decay

B they were hard-bodied

C they were soft-bodied

Many early forms of life didn't form fossils because ☐ .

[Total 1 mark]

2 **Figure 1** shows a fossilised insect preserved in amber (fossilised tree sap).

Figure 1

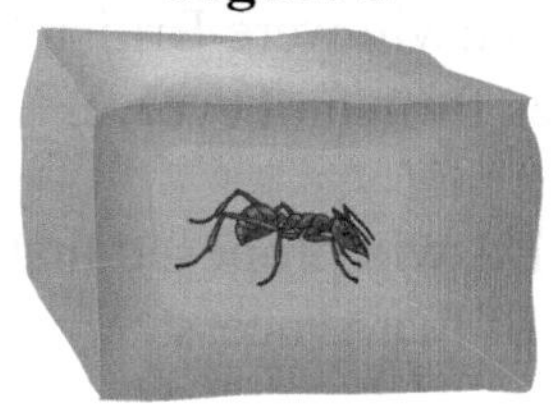

2.1 The fossilised insect in **Figure 1** has been protected from moisture and oxygen.
Explain why this has stopped the insect from decaying.

....

....

[2]

2.2 Traces of organisms can also be considered fossils.
Give **two** examples of a trace which may be left behind by an organism.

1. ....

2. ....

[2]

2.3 Apart from preserved organisms or traces left behind by organisms, give **one** other way in which fossils may be formed.

....

....

[1]

[Total 5 marks]

Speciation

1 Speciation is the development of a new species. Grade 3-4

1.1 Which of the following statements about speciation is correct?
Tick **one** box.

Isolation and natural selection lead to speciation. ☐

Only isolation leads to speciation. ☐

Only natural selection leads to speciation. ☐

[1]

1.2 The statements below describe the steps involved in forming a new species.
Number the boxes **1** to **4** to put the steps in the correct order.

If the two populations meet they will not be able to breed to produce fertile offspring. ☐

A barrier forms between the two populations. ☐

The two populations adapt to their environments. ☐

A large population splits into two populations. ☐

[2]

[Total 3 marks]

2 Alfred Russel Wallace and Charles Darwin were British biologists who carried out work on how species form and evolve. Grade 4-5

2.1 Alfred Russel Wallace and Charles Darwin proposed that evolution took place by one specific process. What is the name of that process?
Tick **one** box.

Normal selection ☐ Natural Variation ☐ Natural selection ☐ Normal variation ☐

[1]

2.2 Which of the following statements is correct?
Tick **one** box.

Alfred Russel Wallace published 'On the Origin of Species' in 1859. ☐

Charles Darwin published 'On the Origin of Species' in 1859. ☐

Alfred Russel Wallace published 'On the Origin of Species' in 1851. ☐

Charles Darwin published 'On the Origin of Species' in 1851. ☐

[1]

2.3 Alfred Russel Wallace worked on the theory of speciation.
State **one** other area of research that he was known for.

....

[1]

[Total 3 marks]

Antibiotic-Resistant Bacteria

Warm-Up

Draw circles to show whether the statements below are **true** or **false**.

Antibiotics are drugs that can kill all pathogens.	True / False
Bacteria can evolve quickly because they divide very rapidly.	True / False
Antibiotic-resistant bacteria don't spread easily.	True / False

1 Bacteria can evolve to become resistant to antibiotics.

Which of the following answers should be used to complete the sentence?
Write **A**, **B** or **C** in the box below.

A normal variation

B natural variation

C natural selection

Bacteria can become resistant to antibiotics by ☐.

[Total 1 mark]

2 *S. aureus* is a bacterium. It can cause serious illness in some people. Some strains of *S. aureus* have developed resistance to the antibiotic meticillin. These strains are known as MRSA.

2.1 **Table 1** shows the different stages that led to *S. aureus* becoming resistant to meticillin. Put the stages in order by writing the correct number (**1**, **2**, **3** or **4**) in the space provided.

Table 1

Number of stage	Stage
....	The gene for meticillin resistance became more common in the population. Eventually most of the population of *S. aureus* had resistance.
....	Individual bacteria with the mutated genes were more likely to survive and reproduce in a host being treated with meticillin.
....	Random mutations in the DNA of *S. aureus* led to it not being killed by meticillin.
....	The gene for meticillin resistance was passed on to lots of offspring. These offspring survived and reproduced.

[2]

2.2 Explain why a person is more likely to become seriously ill if they are infected with MRSA than with a non-resistant strain of *S. aureus*.

....

....

....

[2]

[Total 4 marks]

More on Antibiotic-Resistant Bacteria

1 How can farmers help to prevent the development of antibiotic-resistant bacteria? Tick **one** box. Grade 1-3

By regularly treating their livestock with antibiotics to prevent disease. ☐

By restricting the amount of antibiotics they give to their livestock. ☐

By only using antibiotics to treat viral infections in their livestock. ☐

[Total 1 mark]

2 New antibiotics are being developed against resistant strains of bacteria. Grade 4-5

Give **two** reasons why the development of antibiotics is unlikely to keep up with the rate at which new antibiotic-resistant bacteria appear.

1. ....

2. ....

[Total 2 marks]

3 Antibiotic resistance in bacteria is becoming more common. This is partly due to the overuse of antibiotics in medicine. Grade 4-5

3.1 Give **one** way in which doctors can help to prevent the overuse of antibiotics.

....

....

[1]

A patient has been prescribed antibiotics by his doctor. He needs to take them for two weeks.

After one week, the patient feels better. He wants to stop taking the antibiotics. His doctor tells him he should complete the course.

3.2 Explain why taking the full course of antibiotics reduces the chance of antibiotic-resistant strains developing.

....

....

....

[2]

[Total 3 marks]

Exam Tip

An exam question on antibiotic-resistant bacteria could ask you to link lots of ideas together. So, make sure you know the risks of antibiotic-resistant strains to human health, what's causing them to get more common, and what we can do to prevent them evolving. There's a lot to remember in this topic, but just go over it a few times and you'll be alright.

Target AO3

4 A scientist has samples of two strains of the same species of bacterium, strain A and strain B. This species of bacterium is usually killed by the antibiotic ampicillin, but the scientist believes that strain B may have become resistant to ampicillin.

The scientist has the following materials and equipment:

- nutrient broth solution (culture medium)
- ampicillin solution
- samples of bacterial strain A and strain B, growing in nutrient broth solution
- four small glass bottles, with lids
- pipettes of different sizes

The nutrient broth is clear, but turns cloudy when bacteria grow in it.

4.1 The scientist uses a pipette to add nutrient broth solution to all of the glass bottles. Then he uses another pipette to add ampicillin solution to two of the glass bottles.

Give **one** variable that the scientist should keep the same during this part of the experiment.

....

[1]

4.2* Describe what the scientist should do next in order to find out whether strain B is resistant to ampicillin.

....

....

....

....

....

....

....

....

[4]

4.3 Give **one** reason why it is important that the scientist makes sure that all of the material from the experiment is disposed of safely when it is over.

....

....

[1]

[Total 6 marks]

Exam Tip

You could well be asked to write part of a method for an experiment in your exams. If you are, don't worry. Just think carefully through what you'd need to do if you were actually doing the experiment, then write it all down in a sensible order. Don't forget to use any clues you're given in the question about things like the equipment you might need too.

Classification

Warm-Up

Use the words to complete the Linnaean classification system.
Put the words in the correct order, going from left to right.

species **phylum** **order**

kingdom, ..., class, ..., family, genus, ...

1 Organisms used to be classified into groups using the Linnaean system. Grade 1-3

1.1 Which of the following is the largest group in the Linnaean classification system?
Tick **one** box.

phylum ☐ kingdom ☐ species ☐ genus ☐

[1]

1.2 What does the Linnaean classification system use to classify organisms?
Tick **one** box.

physical characteristics ☐

DNA ☐

the binomial system ☐

[1]

[Total 2 marks]

2 The three-domain classification system was proposed in 1990. Grade 3-4

2.1 What is the name of the scientist who proposed the three-domain system?
Tick **one** box.

Charles Darwin ☐

Carl Woese ☐

Niels Bohr ☐

James Watson ☐

[1]

2.2 Which of the domains includes primitive bacteria often found in extreme environments?

....

[1]

2.3 Give **two** groups of organisms which are in the Eukaryota domain.

1. ....

2. ....

[2]

[Total 4 marks]

3 The black-crested coquette is a species of hummingbird. Its scientific name is *Lophornis helenae*. Grade 4-5

What is the genus of the black-crested coquette?

....

[Total 1 mark]

4 Improvements in our understanding of organisms led to the development of new classification systems, like the three-domain system. Grade 4-5

Give **two** of these improvements.

1. ....

....

2. ....

....

[Total 2 marks]

5 Evolutionary trees show how scientists think that organisms are related to each other. **Figure 1** shows the evolutionary tree for species **A-K**. Grade 4-5

Figure 1

5.1 Give **two** types of data that can be used to make evolutionary trees.

1. ....

2. ....

[2]

5.2 Which species is the most recent common ancestor of species **G** and species **J**?

....

[1]

5.3 Which pair of species, **G** and **H**, or **J** and **K**, are more distantly related?

....

[1]

[Total 4 marks]

Exam Tip

Evolutionary trees are very handy for figuring out how species are related to each other. If you get given an evolutionary tree in the exam, you could be asked to interpret it. But don't worry — just keep practising with questions like these.

Competition

1 There are different levels of organisation within an ecosystem. Grade 1-3

1.1 Which of the following levels of organisation contains the smallest number of organisms?
Tick **one** box.

community ☐

population ☐

ecosystem ☐

[1]

1.2 Which of the following answers should be used to complete the sentence?
Write the correct letter, **A**, **B** or **C**, in the box below.

A one species

B different species

C one population

A community is all the organisms of ☐ living in a habitat.

[1]

[Total 2 marks]

2 **Figure 1** shows a woodland food web. Grade 3-4

Figure 1

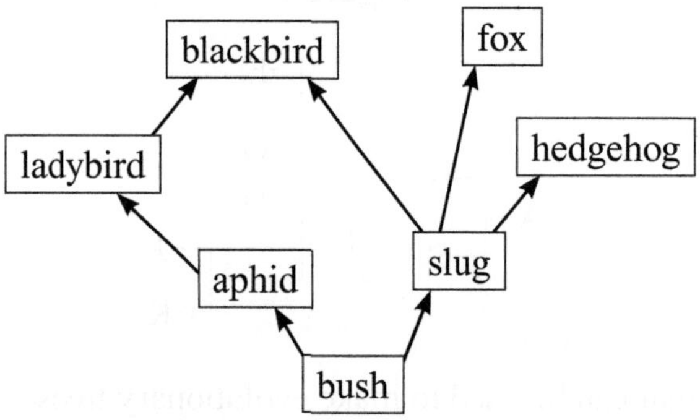

2.1 Which of the following statements is correct?
Tick **one** box.

All the organisms in **Figure 1** are independent. ☐

All the organisms in **Figure 1** are interdependent. ☐

The organisms in **Figure 1** only interact with individuals of the same species. ☐

[1]

2.2 Slugs rely on the bushes for food.
Suggest **one** other factor that slugs may rely on bushes for.

....

[1]

2.3 Apart from food, suggest **two** factors that the **blackbirds** in the ecosystem are likely to compete for.

1. .... 2. ....

[2]

[Total 4 marks]

Abiotic and Biotic Factors

Warm-Up

Biotic factors are the living factors in an environment. Circle **three** biotic factors below.

moisture level   competition   temperature

wind direction   pathogens   predators

1 Abiotic factors can affect the distribution of organisms. (Grade 3-4)

1.1 Which of the following statements is correct? Tick **one** box.

Light intensity and temperature are examples of biotic factors. ☐

Availability of food and carbon dioxide level are examples of abiotic factors. ☐

Light intensity and carbon dioxide level are examples of abiotic factors. ☐

Availability of food and light intensity are examples of biotic factors. ☐

[1]

1.2 Suggest **one** abiotic factor that could affect the distribution of animals living in water.

....

[1]

1.3 Suggest **two** abiotic factors that could affect the distribution of plants growing in soil.

1. ....

2. ....

[2]

[Total 4 marks]

2 A new pathogen is introduced into a population of flowering plants. (Grade 4-5)

2.1 Describe how the introduction of the new pathogen is likely to affect the plant population.

....

....

[1]

2.2 Bees in the ecosystem rely on the flowering plants for a source of food.
Explain how the introduction of the pathogen is likely to affect the bee population.

....

....

[2]

[Total 3 marks]

Exam Tip

Ecology questions in the exam will often ask you about specific organisms — slugs, bees, dandelions, camels, herons, bladderwrack, rat-tailed maggots... Don't worry though — you're not expected to know anything about any particular organism before the exam. These questions are just getting you to apply your knowledge of ecology to real-life examples.

Target AO3

3 The sizes of a population of herons and a population of perch in a lake ecosystem were monitored over ten years. The pH of the lake was also monitored over the same time period. The results are shown in **Figures 1** and **2**.

Figure 1

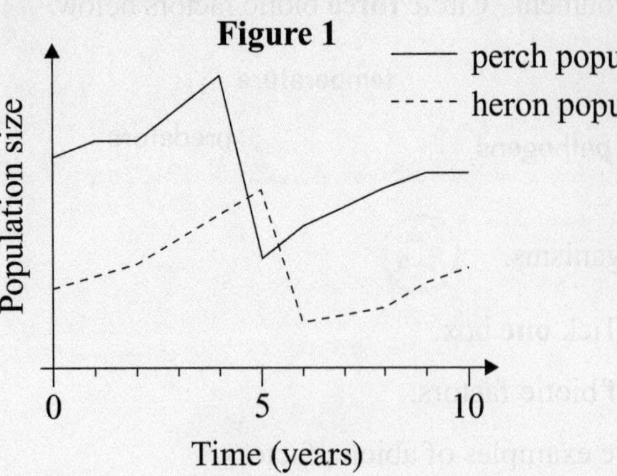

Figure 2

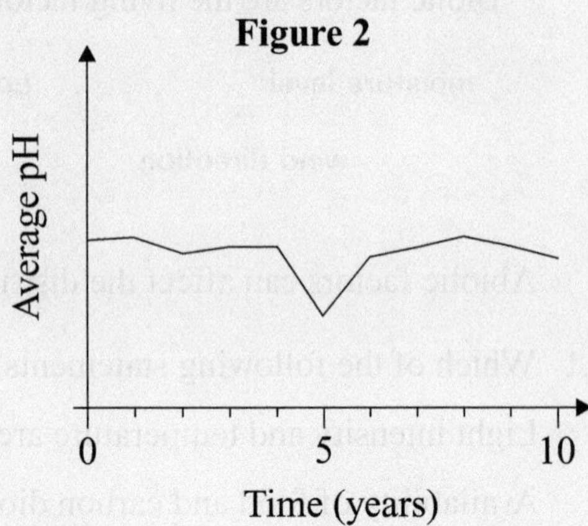

3.1 Describe the trend shown by the heron population in **Figure 1**.

....

....

[1]

A scientist says: 'A fall in the pH level causes perch to die'.

3.2 Suggest how the data in **Figures 1** and **2** supports the scientist's claim.

....

....

....

[2]

3.3 Give **one** reason why the data provided cannot be used to confirm whether the scientist is correct.

....

....

[1]

3.4 A new disease has emerged that is predicted to kill most of the perch in the lake. Using **Figure 1**, suggest and explain what effect the disease is likely to have on the heron population.

....

....

....

[2]

[Total 6 marks]

Exam Tip

If a question in the exam asks you to use some data, make sure you do use it. It's sitting there in a nice little graph or a lovely table, just to help you out, so make the most of it. If you don't use it, you'll miss out on some handy marks.

Adaptations

1 Some organisms live in environments that are very extreme, such as environments with a high salt concentration. Grade 3-4

1.1 What name is given to organisms that live in extreme environments?

....

[1]

1.2 Name **one** group of organisms that can live in deep sea vents where temperatures are very high.

....

[1]

1.3 Describe **one** extreme condition, other than a high salt concentration or a high temperature, that some organisms can tolerate.

....

[1]

[Total 3 marks]

2 Camels live in hot, dry desert conditions.
Table 1 shows some of the adaptations of camels to these conditions. Grade 4-5

Table 1

Adaptation	Reason for adaptation
Long eyelashes	Prevent sand from entering eyes
Very concentrated urine	?
Large surface area to volume ratio	Helps to lose heat
Drinks large quantities of water when available	Helps to replace water lost in hot conditions

2.1 Using **Table 1**, give **one** structural adaptation and **one** behavioural adaptation of the camel.

structural adaptation: ....

behavioural adaptation: ....

[2]

The production of very concentrated urine is a functional adaptation.

2.2 Explain what is meant by a functional adaptation.

....

....

[2]

2.3 Suggest how the production of concentrated urine helps the camel to survive in desert conditions.

....

....

[1]

[Total 5 marks]

Food Chains

Warm-Up

On the food chain below, circle the **producer**.

seaweed → fish → shark → whale

1 **Figure 1** shows an example of a woodland food chain. Grade 3-4

Figure 1

green plants → greenflies → blue tits → sparrowhawk

1.1 Green plants make their own food. What process do they use to do this?

....

[1]

1.2 What term would be used to describe the greenflies' position in **Figure 1**? Tick **one** box.

primary consumer ☐

secondary consumer ☐

tertiary consumer ☐

producer ☐

[1]

1.3 Name **one** organism from **Figure 1** which is a predator.

....

[1]

[Total 3 marks]

2 Foxes are predators. Rabbits are their prey. Grade 4-5

2.1 The number of foxes in an ecosystem increases.
Suggest what will happen to the number of rabbits in the ecosystem. Explain your answer.

....

....

[2]

2.2 A new disease appears in a rabbit population.
Suggest how this could lead to a decrease in the fox population in the same ecosystem.

....

....

....

[2]

[Total 4 marks]

Exam Tip

The arrows in a food chain show the direction of biomass transfer — in other words, they tell you what's eaten by what. For example, greenflies $\xrightarrow{\text{are eaten by}}$ blue tits. It might help you remember this to think 'you $\xrightarrow{\text{are eaten by}}$ the lion'.

Using Quadrats

PRACTICAL

1 A group of students used 1 m^2 quadrats to compare the population sizes of buttercups in two areas of a field. They collected data from three randomly placed quadrats in each area. Their results are shown in **Table 1**.

Table 1

	Quadrat 1	Quadrat 2	Quadrat 3	Mean
Area 1	15	14	13	14
Area 2	26	23	18	**X**

1.1 Calculate the value of **X** in **Table 1**.
Give your answer to 2 significant figures.

X = ...
[2]

1.2 A student says: "The **median** number of buttercups in **Area 1** is 14."
Is she correct? Explain your answer.

....

....
[1]

The students notice that the buttercups in **Area 1** were growing in the shade.
The buttercups in **Area 2** were growing in full sun.

1.3 Another student says:
"The lower light intensity has affected the growth of the buttercups in **Area 1**."
Do you agree with the student? Give a reason for your answer.

....

....
[1]

1.4 **Area 1** has an area of 1750 m^2.
Estimate the total number of buttercups in **Area 1**.

.... buttercups
[1]

[Total 5 marks]

Exam Tip

Make sure you use the right numbers from the data when you're carrying out calculations like the ones above — you don't want to lose marks just for writing down a number wrong. And remember, the first significant figure of a number is the first digit that's not a zero. The second and third significant figures come straight after (even if they are zeros).

PRACTICAL Using Transects

1 **Figure 1** shows a transect line. It is being used to record the distribution of four types of plant in a field.

Figure 1

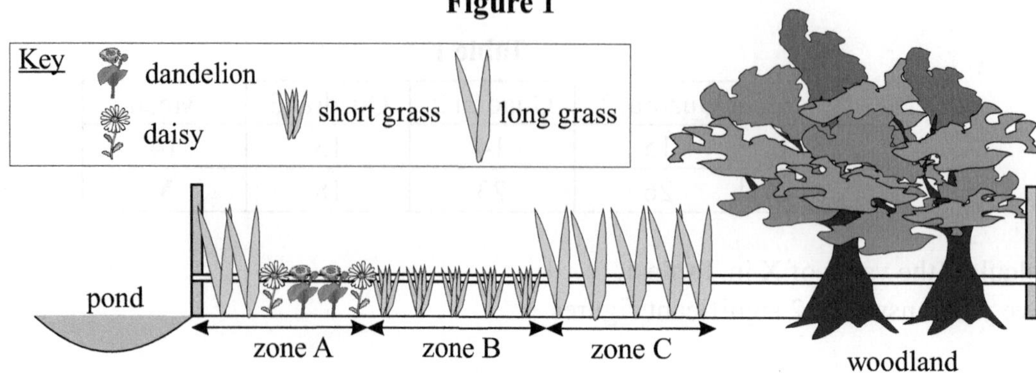

The field is split up into three zones — **A**, **B** and **C**.

1.1 In **Figure 1**, which zones contain only **one** species of plant?

....

[1]

1.2 Dandelions grow best in soils which have a high level of moisture.
Which zone, **A**, **B** or **C**, is most likely to have a high level of moisture?

....

[1]

1.3 Name **one** piece of equipment that may have been used to help collect the information in **Figure 1**.

....

[1]

[Total 3 marks]

2 A student is measuring how much of a habitat is covered by a grass species.
Figure 2 shows the area of a single quadrat covered by the grass.
The quadrat is divided into 100 squares.

Figure 2

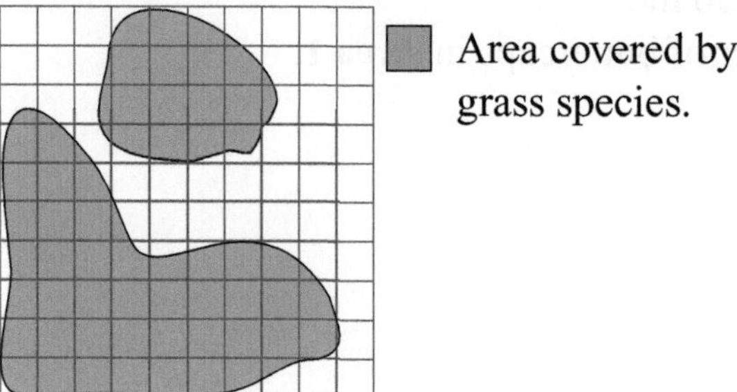

Estimate the percentage area of the quadrat covered by the grass species in **Figure 2**.

Area covered: .... %

[Total 2 marks]

Target AO3

3 A group of students are using a transect to investigate the distribution of organisms across a rocky shore.

Grade 4-5

PRACTICAL

Figure 3 shows a diagram of the shoreline as seen from above. The students plan to place a quadrat at set intervals along the transect and record the species in the quadrat at each point.

Figure 3

3.1 Suggest one hazard that the students should be aware of while carrying out their investigation.

....

.... *[1]*

3.2 The students collect their data by placing a 1 m^2 quadrat at 2 m intervals along the transect and estimating the percentage cover of each organism within the quadrat.

Why might this be a better method than placing the quadrat every metre, with no gap between the intervals? Tick **one** box.

It will make the results more accurate. ☐

It will allow more species to be recorded. ☐

It will take less time to collect the data. ☐

[1]

Table 1 shows the data that the students collected about a seaweed called bladderwrack.

Table 1

Distance from low tide point (m)	2	4	6	8	10	12	14	16	18	20
Percentage cover of bladderwrack in quadrat (%)	0	0	10	10	20	30	40	70	80	60

3.3 Describe the trend in the percentage cover of bladderwrack shown by the data in **Table 1**.

....

....

.... *[2]*

3.4 Suggest **one** way that the students could make sure that their results are repeatable.

.... *[1]*

[Total 5 marks]

Exam Tip

If you have time at the end of the exam, it's always a good idea to have a look back at your answers to make sure that everything you've written is clear and that you've fully answered each question. For example, if a question asked you to describe a trend in some data, make sure you've looked at the right data and that you've actually described the trend.

The Water Cycle

Warm-Up

Find the **three** types of precipitation in the wordsearch below and circle them.

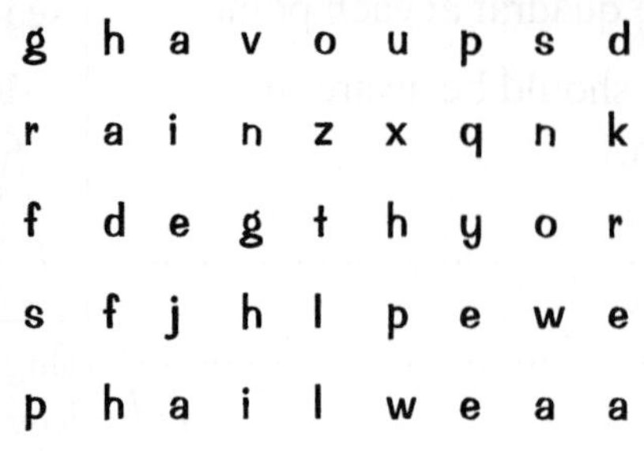

1 **Figure 1** represents the stages in the water cycle.

Figure 1

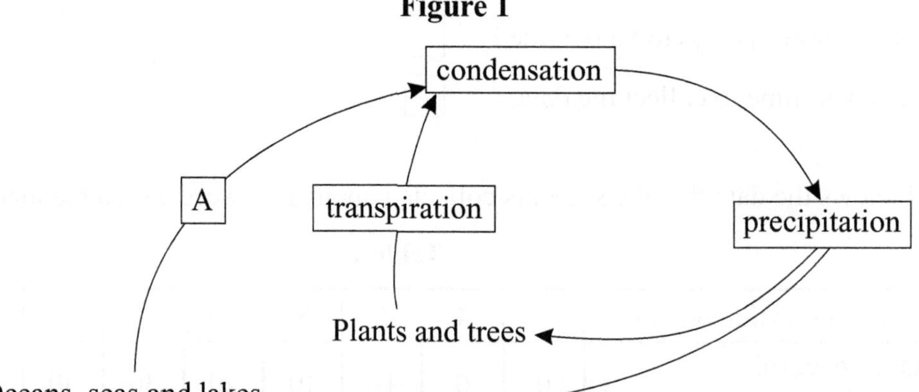

1.1 Name the process represented by **A** in the diagram.

.... *[1]*

1.2 What is meant by the term 'precipitation'?

.... *[1]*

1.3 Explain why precipitation is an important stage in the water cycle.

....

.... *[1]*

1.4 Suggest how the water in plants can be passed on to animals.

.... *[1]*

[Total 4 marks]

The Carbon Cycle

1 Figure 1 shows a simplified version of the carbon cycle. 

Figure 1

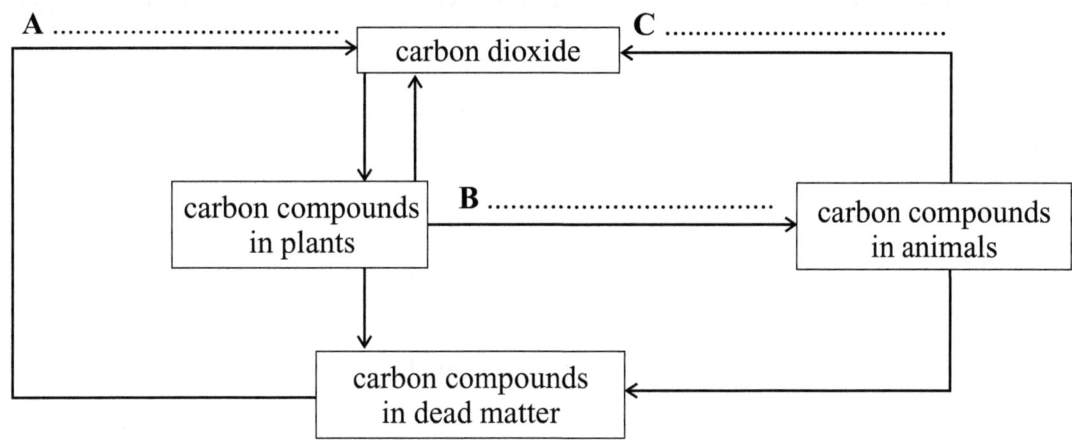

Complete **Figure 1**.
Fill in the labels **A**, **B** and **C** using words from the box.

decay	**respiration**	**eating**	**photosynthesis**

[Total 3 marks]

2 The carbon cycle describes how carbon moves between organisms and their environment. 

2.1 Explain how microorganisms in the soil release carbon from dead matter.

....

....

[2]

2.2 Describe how carbon from the air can become a part of the carbon compounds in a plant.

....

....

....

....

[3]

[Total 5 marks]

Exam Tip

Make sure you know all of the carbon cycle, not just bits of it. Sketching it out might help you to remember it. First, write down all of the different places that the carbon can be, e.g. in the air, in plants. Then add the processes that move the carbon between these places, e.g. respiration. Add arrows to show which way the carbon in each process is moving.

Decay

Warm-Up

Circle which household wastes are only made up of organic matter.

Grass cuttings and food peelings. | Food peelings and empty tin cans. | Empty tin cans and plastic detergent bottles.

1 Biogas is a fuel produced by the breakdown of organic waste by microorganisms such as bacteria. It is made up of several gases.

Grade 4-5

1.1 What is the main gas found in biogas? Tick **one** box.

oxygen ☐ methane ☐ hydrogen ☐ carbon dioxide ☐

[1]

1.2 Which of the following statements is correct? Tick **one** box.

Biogas is produced by aerobic decay. ☐ Biogas is produced by anaerobic decay. ☐

[1]

Figure 1 shows a biogas generator. It is built underground to help stop the organic waste from getting too hot.

Figure 1

1.3 Why should the organic waste not get too hot?

....

....

[1]

Gardeners use the breakdown of organic waste to produce compost.

1.4 What do gardeners use compost for?

....

[1]

1.5 Gardeners control temperature and the availability of oxygen to help produce compost quickly. Give **one** other condition that gardeners might control.

....

[1]

1.6 How does the condition you gave in **1.5** affect the rate of decay? Explain your answer.

....

....

[2]

[Total 7 marks]

Exam Tip

Decay isn't the most glamorous thing ever, but it's a very important process. If you want to speed up the decay process (e.g. if you're making compost), you'll need to make sure that everything is just how the decay microorganisms like it. In the exam, you might be asked what factors can affect the rate of decay. So make sure that you know.

Investigating Decay

1 A student was investigating the effect of temperature on the decay of milk by an enzyme. Grade 4-5

1. He added an indicator solution to a sample of alkaline milk in a test tube. He then placed it in a water bath.
2. When the mixture in the tube reached the desired temperature, he added some lipase enzyme solution.
3. As the lipase broke down the milk, a colour change occurred.
4. He timed how long it took for the colour change to occur at four different temperatures. **Table 1** shows his results.

Table 1

Temperature (°C)	Mean time taken for colour change to occur (s)
10	294
20	258
30	238
40	**X**

1.1 Why did a colour change occur as the lipase broke down the milk?

....

[1]

Table 2 shows the results of three repeats carried out at 40 °C.

Table 2

Temperature (°C)	Time taken for colour change to occur (s)			
	1st repeat	2nd repeat	3rd repeat	Mean
40	217	224	219	**X**

1.2 Calculate the mean time taken for the colour change to occur at 40 °C (**X**).

.... s

[1]

Figure 1

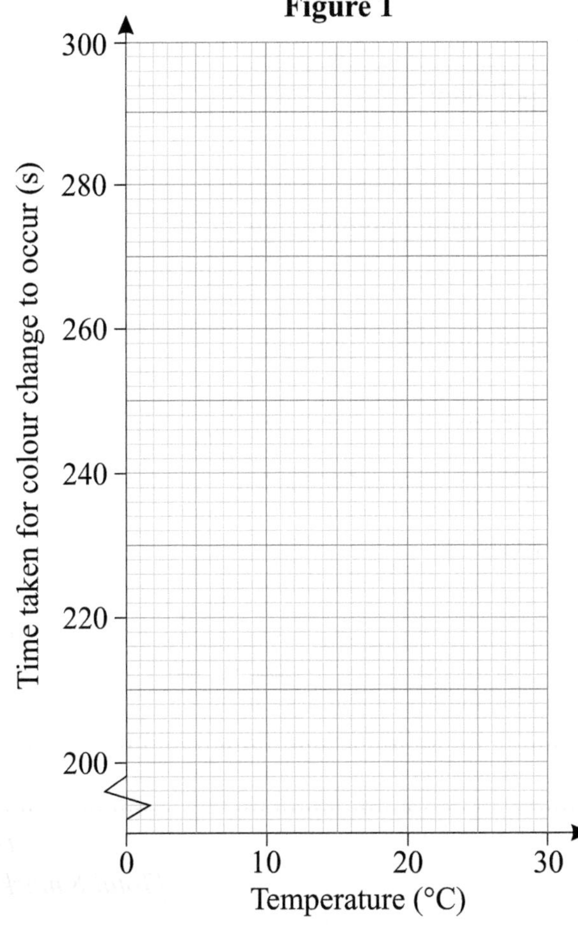

Figure 1 is an incomplete graph. It shows the mean time taken for the colour change to occur against temperature.

1.3 Complete **Figure 1**. Plot the mean time taken for the colour change to occur at each temperature from **10 °C** to **30 °C**.

[1]

1.4 What does the completed graph show about the relationship between temperature and the rate of decay? Tick **one** box.

There is no relationship. ☐

As temperature increases, the rate of decay increases. ☐

As temperature increases, the rate of decay decreases. ☐

[1]

[Total 4 marks]

Biodiversity and Waste Management

1 Many scientists are interested in the biodiversity of ecosystems. 

Complete the sentences below about biodiversity.
Use answers from the box.

species	**more**	**less**	**habitats**	**plants**

Biodiversity is the variety of different .... in an ecosystem.

An ecosystem with a high biodiversity is .... stable than an ecosystem with a low biodiversity.

[Total 2 marks]

2 The global population is using an increasing amount of resources. Grade 4-5

2.1 State **two** reasons why humans are using more resources.

1. ....

2. ....

[2]

People are also creating more waste and more pollution.
Table 1 shows three different parts of the environment that can become polluted.

Table 1

	Types of pollutant
Air	1. smoke 2. ....
Land	1. pesticides 2. ....
Water	1. .... 2. ....

2.2 Complete **Table 1** to show examples of the different types of pollutant that can affect air, land and water.

[4]

2.3 Explain how pollution affects biodiversity.

....

....

[2]

[Total 8 marks]

Target AO3

3 The presence of indicator species in an area can provide evidence for the level of pollution in the ecosystem. A student is surveying the numbers of three indicator species in two small rivers as a measure of water pollution.

This is the method that the student used:

1. Place a long-handled net with a fine mesh on the bottom of the river. It should be positioned so that water is flowing into the net.
2. Stand upstream of the net and gently disturb the bottom of the river by moving your feet for 30 seconds.
3. Empty the contents of the net into a large tray filled with a 3 cm depth of water.
4. Identify and count the individuals of the indicator species in your sample.
5. Empty the contents of the tray back into the river.

Table 2 shows the results. **Table 3** gives details of the indicator species.

Table 2

Individuals counted in survey	River 1	River 2
freshwater shrimp	29	0
water louse	60	10
rat-tailed maggot	4	88

Table 3

Indicator species	Presence of species indicates:
freshwater shrimp	low level of pollution
water louse	medium level of pollution
rat-tailed maggot	high level of pollution

3.1 State an appropriate way to display the results in **Table 2**.

....

[1]

3.2 Use the results to decide which of the statements below is correct. Tick **one** box.

River 2 is more polluted than River 1 because there are more freshwater shrimp. ☐

Water lice are found in both rivers, so the rivers are equally polluted. ☐

River 1 is less polluted than River 2 because there are fewer rat-tailed maggots. ☐

All three indicator species are present in River 1, so it isn't polluted. ☐

[1]

3.3 A factory discharges waste water into another small river, River 3.
A local newspaper claims that the waste water is causing an increase in pollution in the river.
The student plans to use the method outlined above to investigate the claim.

State **two** locations that the student would need to survey in her investigation.

1. ....

2. ....

[2]

[Total 4 marks]

Exam Tip

In your exams, you could be given the method for an experiment and asked how you could adapt it to test a different hypothesis. You'll need to have a think about what the original method was testing. Then have a good read of the new hypothesis you've been given, and work out what things you'd need to change in order to test that instead.

 ☐  ☐  ☐

Global Warming

Warm-Up

The sentences below are to do with global warming.
Circle **one** underlined phrase in each sentence, so that the sentence is correct.

<u>Carbon dioxide</u> / <u>Sulfur dioxide</u> is a greenhouse gas.

<u>Oxygen</u> / <u>Methane</u> is also a greenhouse gas.

The levels of these greenhouse gases are <u>decreasing</u> / <u>increasing</u>.

This is <u>cooling down</u> / <u>heating up</u> the Earth.

1 **Figure 1** shows the distribution of a butterfly species in Britain in 1986 and in 2016.

Figure 1

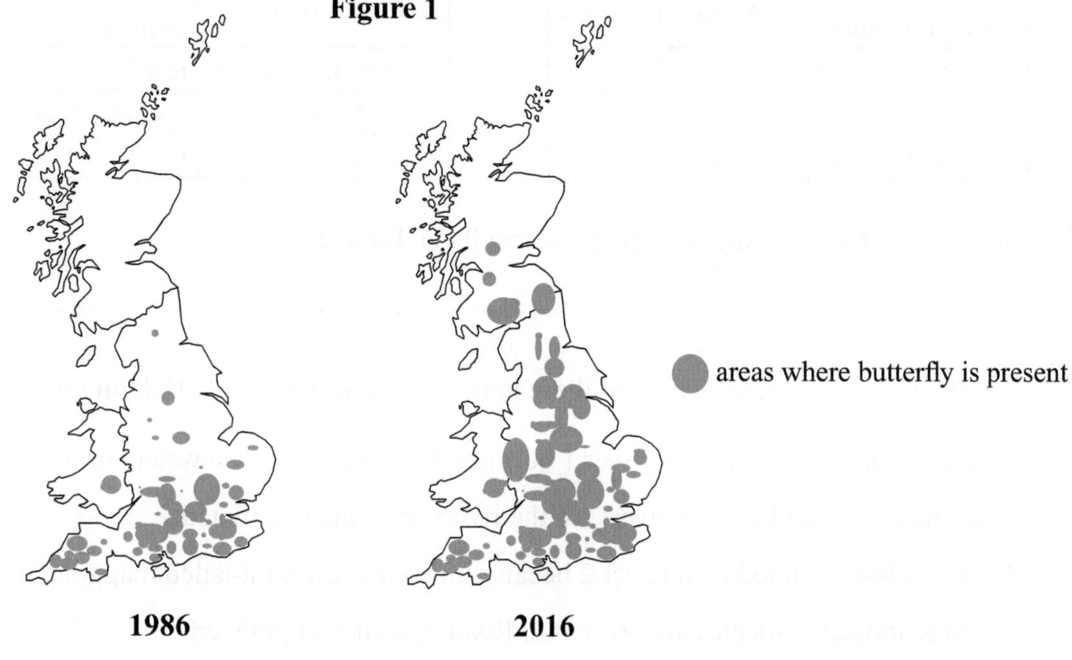

1.1 Give **two** ways in which the distribution of the butterfly species changed between 1986 and 2016.

1. ....

2. ....

[2]

1.2 A scientist thinks that the change in the distribution of the butterfly is due to global warming.

Suggest **one** other piece of data the scientist might need to find out if she is correct.

....

[1]

[Total 3 marks]

Exam Tip

Greenhouse gases cause the 'greenhouse effect'. Without greenhouse gases trapping energy in the Earth's atmosphere, it'd be too cold for us to survive. But as we do things that increase the amounts of these gases in the atmosphere, the amount of energy that they trap is increasing too. That's why we're getting all hot and bothered about them...

Deforestation and Land Use

1 The destruction of peat bogs can lead to problems. Grade 1-3

1.1 How can peat be used by humans?
Tick **one** box.

as a cleaning product ☐

as an animal feed ☐

as a pesticide ☐

as a compost ☐

[1]

When harvesting peat, peat bogs are drained before the peat is removed. Because the bogs are drained, any peat left behind will begin to decay.

1.2 What gas is released when peat decays?
Tick **one** box.

carbon monoxide ☐ carbon dioxide ☐ nitrogen ☐ oxygen ☐

[1]

1.3 What problem does the release of the gas you named in **1.2** contribute to?

....

[1]

[Total 3 marks]

2 Human activity reduces the amount of land available for other animals and plants. Grade 4-5

2.1 Give **two** uses of land by humans.

1. ....

2. ....

[2]

Areas of land are often deforested so that they can be used by humans.

2.2 Give **one** reason why an area of land in the tropics may be deforested.

....

....

[1]

2.3 What effect does deforestation have on biodiversity in an area? Give a reason for your answer.

Effect: ....

Reason: ....

....

[2]

[Total 5 marks]

 ☐  ☐  ☐

Maintaining Ecosystems and Biodiversity

1 A farmer grows a single type of crop.
As a result, her fields have a low biodiversity. Grade 3-4

What could the farmer do to increase the biodiversity of her fields?
Tick **two** boxes.

Replace the fences around her fields with hedgerows. ☐

Cut down trees around the edges of her fields. ☐

Increase her use of chemical pesticides. ☐

Allow wild flowers and grasses to grow around the edges of her fields. ☐

Reduce her use of chemical fertilisers. ☐

[Total 2 marks]

2 In some areas, programmes have been put in place to reduce the negative effects of human activity on ecosystems and biodiversity. Grade 4-5

2.1 Which of the following could reduce carbon dioxide emissions into the atmosphere?
Tick **one** box.

Setting up more breeding programmes for endangered species. ☐

Using more land for landfill sites. ☐

Increasing the number of power stations. ☐

Reducing deforestation. ☐

[1]

2.2 The government encourages people to recycle as much of their waste as possible.
Suggest how this could help to protect ecosystems.

....

....

[2]

2.3 Breeding programmes are carried out in zoos in many countries.
Suggest how breeding programmes in zoos could increase biodiversity in the wild.

....

....

[2]

[Total 5 marks]

Exam Tip

Humans do a lot to reduce biodiversity (boo, hiss). But remember — there are also lots of ways that we can have a positive effect on it. Make sure that you can describe a few different methods for protecting or increasing biodiversity. You should be able to explain how the different methods that you've described work, too.

Trophic Levels

Warm-Up

The diagram below shows some of the feeding relationships in a rocky shore environment. Sort the organisms into the columns of the table. Each organism belongs in only one column.

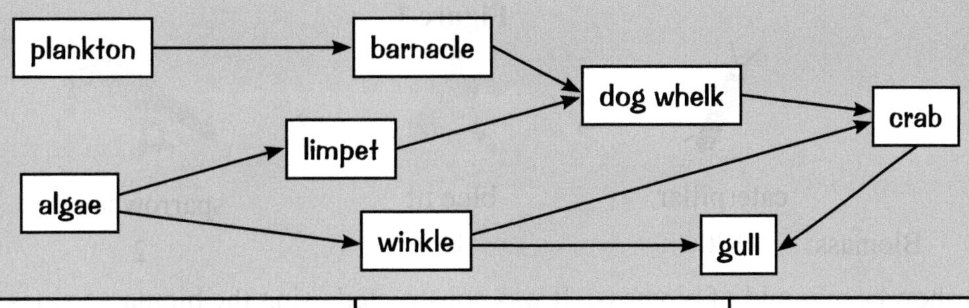

Producer	Herbivore	Carnivore

1 Decomposers play an important role in ecosystems.

What do decomposers do in an ecosystem? Tick **one** box.

Break down dead plant or animal material. ☐

Photosynthesise their own food. ☐

They act as secondary consumers. ☐

They eat plants and algae. ☐

[Total 1 mark]

2 The trophic levels in a food chain can be represented by numbers, starting at level 1 with producers.

2.1 Which of the following organisms would be found at level 2? Tick **one** box.

☐ photosynthetic organisms ☐ carnivores ☐ herbivores ☐ decomposers

[1]

2.2 Some carnivores eat other carnivores. Which level represents these carnivores? Tick **one** box.

☐ level 1 ☐ level 2 ☐ level 3 ☐ level 4

[1]

2.3 What is an apex predator?

....

[1]

[Total 3 marks]

Exam Tip

When it comes to trophic levels, there are quite a lot of terms to learn — producers, decomposers, primary, secondary and tertiary consumers, apex predators, carnivores and herbivores. Make sure you know what they all mean before you get to exam day. Answering trophic level questions will be much, much easier if you've got these key terms nailed.

Pyramids of Biomass

1 Pyramids of biomass show the relative amount of biomass in each level of a food chain. 

Figure 1 shows part of a food chain from an area of oak woodland.
The biomass values are given in arbitrary units.

Figure 1

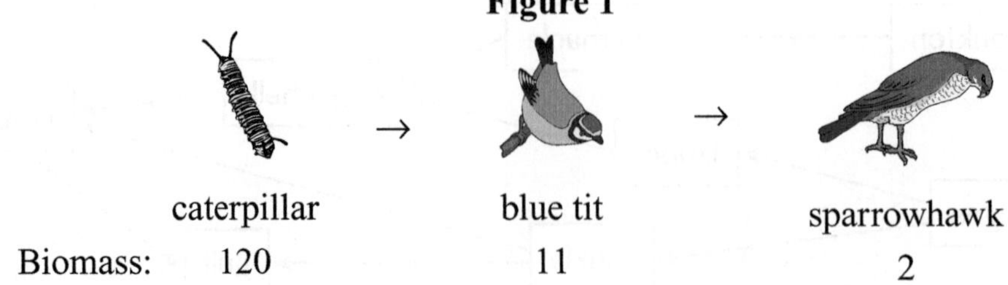

Figure 2 shows a pyramid of biomass. It was constructed using the biomass values from **Figure 1**.

Figure 2

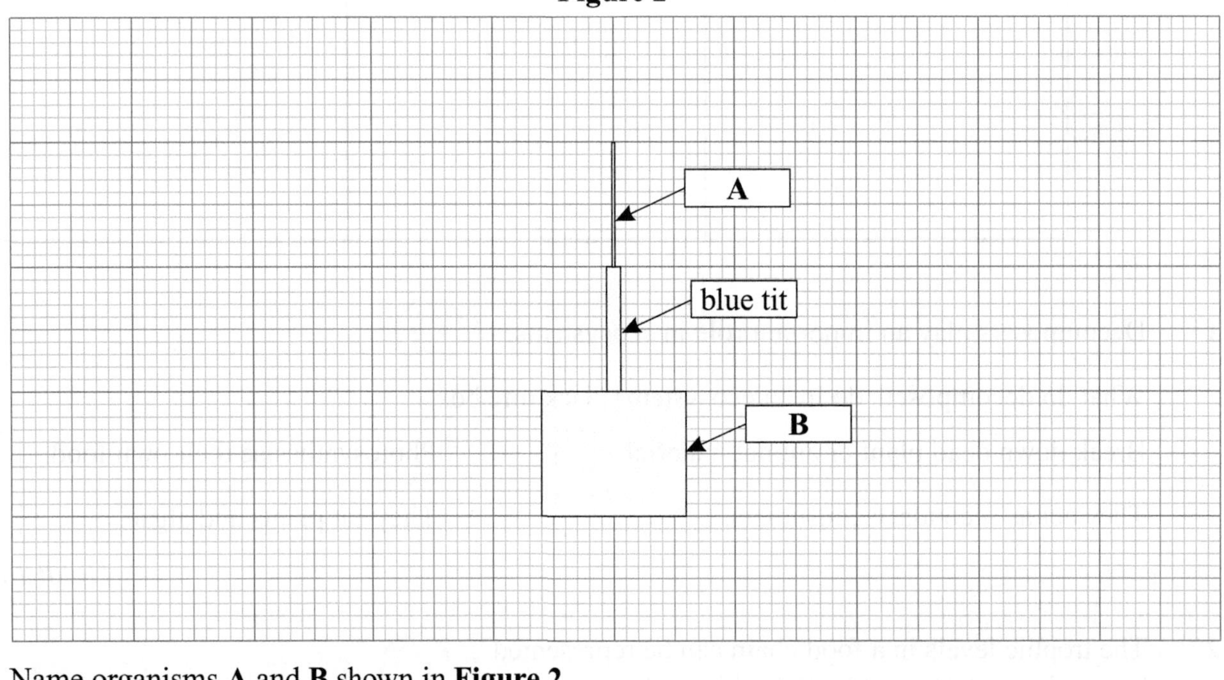

1.1 Name organisms **A** and **B** shown in **Figure 2**.

A: .... **B**: ....

[1]

1.2 The producer in the food chain shown in **Figure 1** is an oak tree. The oak tree has a biomass of **1000** arbitrary units. Draw a bar on **Figure 2** to show the biomass of this oak tree.

[2]

1.3 Biomass decreases as the trophic level increases. Using this information, suggest why there are usually only four or five trophic levels in a food chain.

....

....

[1]

[Total 4 marks]

Exam Tip

It's a good idea to take a sharp pencil, a ruler and an eraser into the exam (as well as your lucky pen, of course). Other things that might come in handy include: a calculator, a spare pen, a tissue, a bottle of water and a kitten* (for the stress).

*CGP disclaimer: please don't actually take a kitten into the exam with you. You will get in trouble. And the kitten won't like it...

Target AO3

2 A student wants to estimate the total biomass of dandelions in the school field. (Grade 4-5)

The student writes the following method:

1. Pick a dandelion flower from the field and dry it in an oven for 2 hours.
2. Weigh the dandelion to find the dry biomass of one plant.
3. Place a 1 m^2 quadrat in several areas of the field where dandelions are visible and record the number of dandelions in the quadrat.
4. Work out the mean number of dandelions in a square metre, then multiply that number by the area of the field.

2.1 The student's teacher points out some errors in her method.
Which of these statements are errors in her method? Tick **two** boxes.

The biomass of the whole plant isn't being measured. ☐

It will be too difficult to accurately count all the dandelions in a 1 m^2 quadrat. ☐

She should divide the mean number of dandelions in a square metre by the area of the field. ☐

The quadrats should be placed in random locations in the field. ☐

[2]

2.2 The teacher also says that the student should measure the biomass of more than one dandelion and work out the average biomass of a plant.
Give **one** reason why using a larger sample size could improve the student's investigation.

....

[1]

2.3 Dandelions are a source of food for many organisms. Why should the student **not** measure the biomass of a very large number of dandelions from the field? Tick **one** box.

It would make the results of the experiment less accurate. ☐

Picking too many could negatively affect the ecosystem. ☐

There would be no biomass left in the field. ☐

The sample size would be too large to be representative. ☐

[1]

2.4 The student's method allows her to calculate the population size of dandelions in the field.
Describe what she would need to do next in order to estimate the total biomass of dandelions in the field.

....

....

[1]

[Total 5 marks]

Exam Tip

It's not just good science and fair tests that you have to think about when you're doing experiments — the examiners may well want to know that you can think about health and safety, ethics, and the knock-on effects of what you're doing as well. After all, it wouldn't look too good if you destroyed an entire forest just to count the number of snails in it.

Biomass Transfer

1 Not all material that is eaten is used by the body. Grade 4-5

1.1 What happens to ingested material that does not get absorbed?

....

[1]

1.2 Name **two** substances lost as waste in urine.

....

[2]

[Total 3 marks]

2 There are losses of biomass at each trophic level in a food chain. Grade 4-5

2.1 Which of the following is **not** a way that biomass can be lost? Tick **one** box.

Through urine. ☐

Through waste substances from respiration. ☐

Through waste substances from photosynthesis. ☐

[1]

Table 1 shows the amount of biomass available at each trophic level in a food chain.

Table 1

Trophic level	1	2	3	4
Biomass available (arbitrary units)	55.30	6.40	0.60	0.06
Efficiency of biomass transfer (%)	–	11.6	9.4	**X**

The efficiency of biomass transfer between trophic levels can be calculated by using the equation:

$$\text{efficiency} = \frac{\text{biomass transferred to next level}}{\text{biomass available at the previous level}} \times 100$$

2.2 Calculate the value of **X** in **Table 1**. Complete the steps below.

Write down the biomass transferred from **trophic level 3** to **trophic level 4**.

....

Write down the biomass available at **trophic level 3**.

....

Work out the efficiency of biomass transfer.

.... %

[2]

[Total 3 marks]

Exam Tip

Remember, biomass transfers are <u>not</u> very efficient. If you're asked to calculate the efficiency of a biomass transfer in the exam and your answer tells you the transfer is 99% efficient, you should probably take another look at your working...

Food Security and Farming

1 Several factors affect food security. Grade 4-5

1.1 What is 'food security'?

....

[1]

1.2 Which of the following factors is **not** a threat to food security?
Tick **one** box.

- [ ] A new disease that affects crops.
- [ ] Conflict over resources.
- [ ] Decreasing birth rate.
- [ ] High costs of farming.

[1]

1.3 Give **one** example of an environmental change that could affect food production.

....

[1]

[Total 3 marks]

2 Fish stocks around the world are monitored regularly. Grade 4-5

2.1 Overfishing can reduce the size of fish stocks.
What effect could this have on food security?

....

[1]

2.2 Explain your answer to question **2.1**.

....

....

[1]

2.3* Give **two** methods that can be used to try to conserve fish stocks at a sustainable level.
Explain how these methods can help to conserve fish stocks.

....

....

....

....

....

....

[4]

[Total 6 marks]

3 Fish can be bred in fish farms, as shown in **Figure 1**. Grade 4-5

Figure 1

3.1 In some fish farms, the fish are kept very close together. Suggest **one** disadvantage of keeping animals close together in a fish farm.

....

....

[1]

3.2 In fish farms, the movement of fish is restricted. This reduces the transfer of energy from the fish to the environment. Why might fish farmers want to reduce this transfer of energy?

....

....

....

[2]

[Total 3 marks]

4 A scientist researched the amount of animal feed needed to produce 1 kg of three different types of meats on a farm. At this farm, the animals were kept outside and had large enclosures. **Table 1** shows the results. Grade 4-5

Table 1

Animal	Chicken	Pigs	Cattle
Amount of feed needed to produce 1 kg meat	2.1 kg	4.1 kg	10.5 kg

4.1 The scientist concluded that the chicken was the most efficient food source. Suggest why this was the scientist's conclusion.

....

[1]

4.2 The scientist repeated his investigation at a farm where the animals were kept in small indoor pens. State whether these animals would likely need more or less feed to produce 1 kg of meat. Explain your answer.

....

....

....

[2]

[Total 3 marks]

Exam Tip

When you're faced with a difficult-looking question, try underlining the key words to help you focus on what you're actually being asked about (e.g. you could have underlined small indoor pens in question 4.2). By finding the key words, you'll be less likely to either mis-read the question or start writing about something that isn't really relevant.

Biotechnology

1 Some organisms can be genetically modified to produce desired substances. (Grade 4-5)

1.1 Give **one** use for genetically modified bacteria.

....

[1]

1.2 Suggest **two** advantages of genetically modified crops.

....

....

[2]

[Total 3 marks]

2 A fungus called *Fusarium* is used to produce protein-rich foods suitable for vegetarians. (Grade 4-5)

2.1 What is the name of the product that can be produced by this fungus?
Tick **one** box.

☐ insulin ☐ protein ☐ mycoprotein ☐ biomass

[1]

The fungus is grown on glucose syrup in a fermenter. **Figure 1** shows this process.

Figure 1

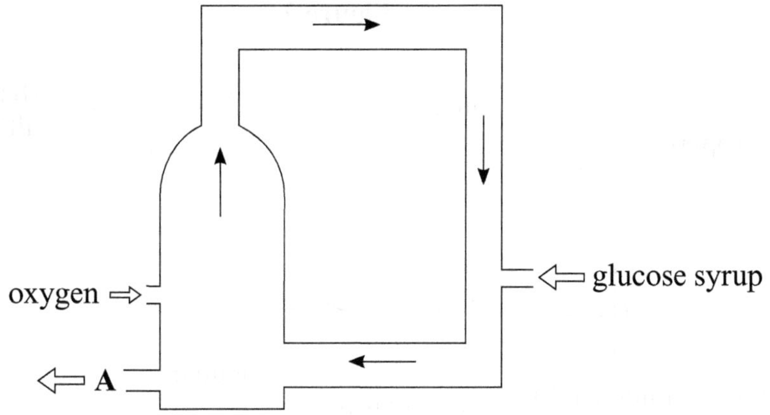

2.2 Which of the following options best describes the conditions in the fermenter?
Tick **one** box.

☐ anaerobic ☐ aerobic ☐ both anaerobic and aerobic

[1]

2.3 Suggest what happens at point **A** in **Figure 1**.

....

[1]

2.4 What is the role of the glucose syrup in the fermenter?

....

[1]

[Total 4 marks]

Mixed Questions

1 **Figure 1** shows a type of animal cell. Grade 1-3

Figure 1

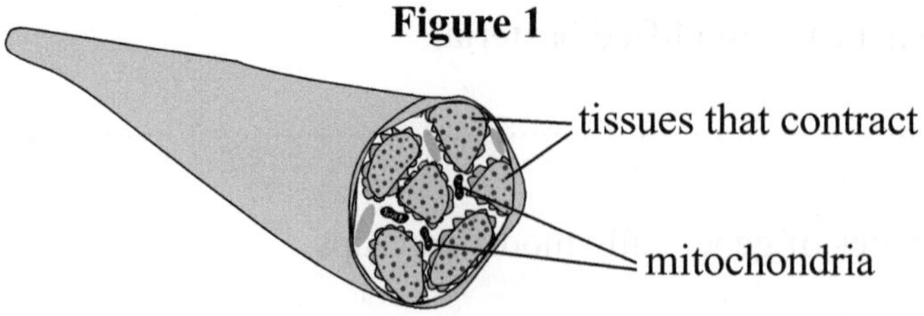

1.1 What type of cell is the cell in **Figure 1**? Tick **one** box.

sperm cell ☐ nerve cell ☐ muscle cell ☐ xylem cell ☐

[1]

1.2 Why does this type of cell have lots of mitochondria? Tick **one** box.

To provide the energy the cell needs to carry out its function. ☐

To allow the cell to carry out photosynthesis. ☐

To allow the cell to produce lots of proteins. ☐

To strengthen the cell. ☐

[1]

Figure 2 shows a single-celled organism called *Euglena*, found in pond water. *Euglena* is a eukaryote.

Figure 2

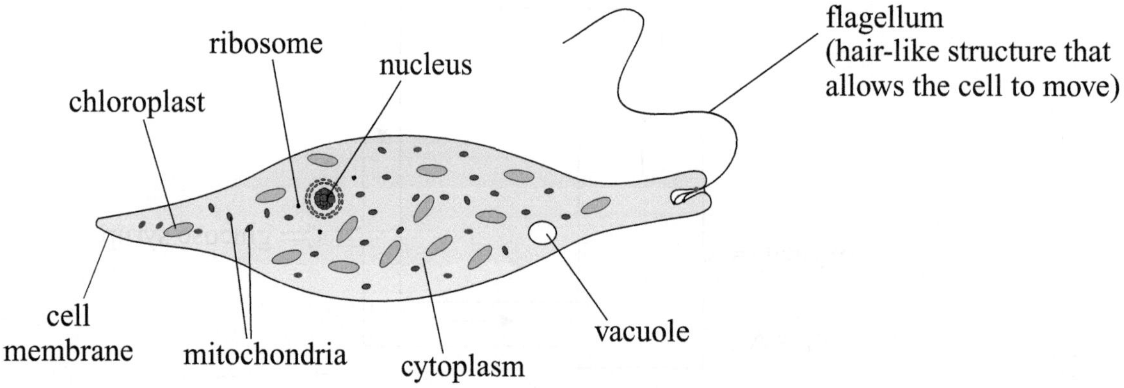

1.3 Give **one** piece of evidence from **Figure 2** which shows that *Euglena* is a eukaryote and not a prokaryote.

....

[1]

[Total 3 marks]

2 One of the functions of the liver is to break down excess amino acids. Grade 1-3

2.1 Which of the following molecules is made up of amino acids? Tick **one** box.

a carbohydrate ☐ a protein ☐ a lipid ☐ glycerol ☐

[1]

2.2 State **one** function of the liver, other than breaking down amino acids.

....

[1]

2.3 Urea is a waste product from the breakdown of amino acids.
Which organ removes urea from the body? Tick **one** box.

brain ☐ pancreas ☐ kidney ☐ lung ☐

[1]

[Total 3 marks]

3 Aerobic respiration transfers energy from glucose. Grade 3-4

3.1 Complete the word equation for aerobic respiration.

glucose + ... → .... + water

[2]

3.2 Glucose is transported around the body in the blood.

The steps below describe what happens when the blood glucose level gets too high.

Put the steps in order by writing the correct number (**1**, **2**, **3** or **4**) in the space provided.

.... The pancreas releases insulin.

.... Glucose is converted into glycogen for storage.

.... Glucose moves into the liver and muscle cells.

.... Receptors in the pancreas detect that the blood glucose level is too high.

[2]

[Total 4 marks]

4 In pea plants, seed shape is controlled by a single gene. Grade 3-4

The allele for round seed shape is R. The allele for wrinkled seed shape is r.
R is a dominant allele and r is recessive.

4.1 What is the **genotype** of a pea plant that is homozygous dominant for seed shape?

RR ☐ rr ☐ wrinkled ☐ round ☐

[1]

4.2 What is the **phenotype** of a pea plant that is homozygous dominant for seed shape?

RR ☐ rr ☐ wrinkled ☐ round ☐

[1]

Exam Tip

Phenotype and genotype are easy words to get mixed up, but they mean different things. If they crop up in the exam, make sure you're definitely using the right one to answer the question — otherwise you won't get the marks.

Two pea plants with a heterozygous genotype were crossed.
Figure 3 shows an incomplete Punnett square of this cross.

4.3 Complete the Punnett square to show the possible genotypes of the offspring.

Figure 3

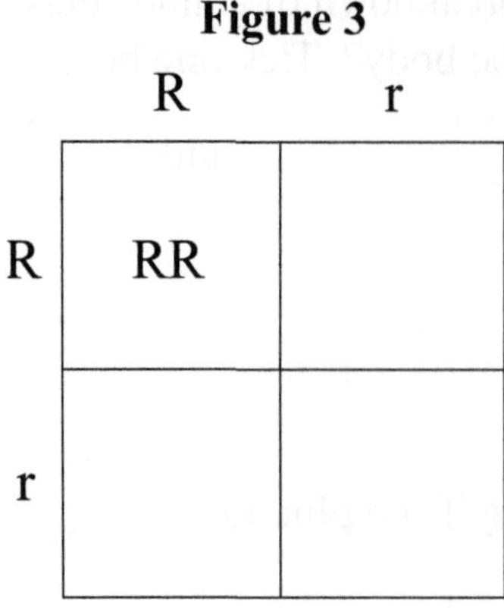

	R	r
R	RR	
r		

[1]

4.4 If four pea plants are produced from the cross, how many of them would you expect to have wrinkled seeds?

1 ☐ 2 ☐ 3 ☐ 4 ☐

[1]

[Total 4 marks]

5 **Figure 4** shows a plant cell with one of its subcellular structures magnified. The overall movement of four molecules into and out of the subcellular structure is also shown.

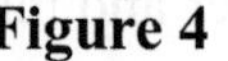

Figure 4

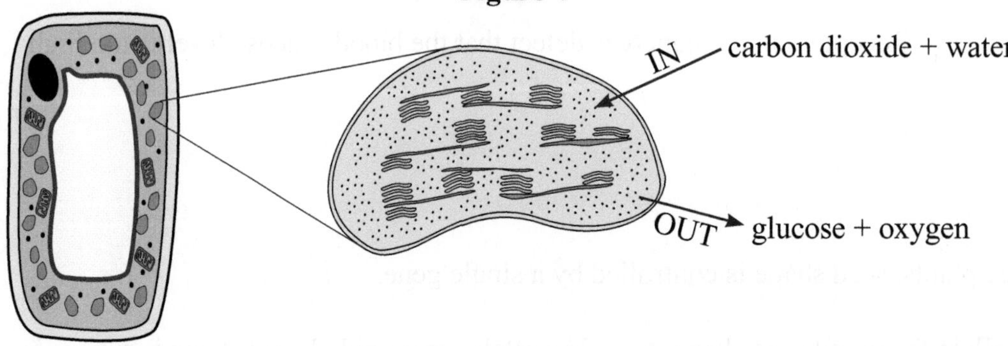

5.1 Look at the movements of carbon dioxide, water, glucose and oxygen in **Figure 4**. What reaction do these movements suggest is taking place in the magnified subcellular structure?

....

[1]

5.2 What is the name of the magnified subcellular structure in **Figure 4**?

....

[1]

5.3 The width of the image of the subcellular structure when viewed using a microscope is 45 mm. What is the width of the magnified image in μm?
Tick **one** box.

45 000 μm ☐ 0.045 μm ☐ 4500 μm ☐ 4.5 μm ☐

[1]

The cell in **Figure 4** is from a leaf.

5.4 Describe how carbon dioxide enters a leaf.

....

....

[2]

5.5 What is the name of the process which transports water up a plant and into the leaves?

....

[1]

5.6 After glucose has been produced by a plant cell, some of it leaves the cell to be transported around the plant. What is the name of the transportation process?

....

[1]

[Total 7 marks]

6 Alcohol dehydrogenase enzymes break down alcohol in the body. Grade 4-5

6.1 Which of the following sentences about enzymes is correct? Tick **one** box.

Enzymes speed up chemical reactions in living organisms. ☐

Enzymes are used up in chemical reactions. ☐

Enzymes are products of digestion. ☐

Enzymes are the building blocks of all living organisms. ☐

[1]

A scientist was investigating the effect of pH on the rate of activity of alcohol dehydrogenase. **Figure 5** shows a graph of his results.

Figure 5

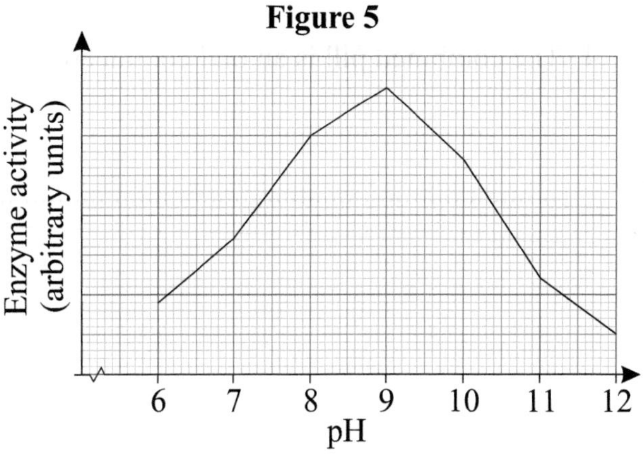

6.2 What is the optimum pH for the enzyme?

....

[1]

6.3 Suggest and explain the effect an acid with a pH of 1 would have on the enzyme.

....

....

....

[3]

Exam Tip

In your exam, you could be asked to 'suggest and explain' something. 'Suggest' is just asking you to take what you know and apply it to a new situation. Then 'explain' your thinking — say why you made the suggestion that you did.

6.4 Which of the following statements about alcohol is correct? Tick **one** box.

Alcohol is a risk factor for several communicable diseases. ☐

Alcohol is a risk factor for lung cancer. ☐

Alcohol can cause liver damage. ☐

Alcohol has no effect on brain function. ☐

[1]

[Total 6 marks]

7 The endocrine system uses hormones to produce effects within the body. Grade 4-5

7.1 Describe how a hormone travels from a gland to its target organ in the body.

....

....

[2]

7.2 What is the main function of progesterone? Tick **one** box.

To cause the egg to mature. ☐ To maintain the uterus lining. ☐

To stimulate the release of the egg. ☐ To stimulate sperm production. ☐

[1]

7.3 Where in the body is oestrogen produced? Tick **one** box.

pituitary gland ☐ testes ☐ thyroid ☐ ovaries ☐

[1]

7.4 The combined pill is an oral contraceptive. Explain how oral contraceptives prevent pregnancy.

....

....

[2]

[Total 6 marks]

8 A scientist was investigating two plant diseases caused by bacteria. Grade 4-5

Bacterial canker is a plant disease caused by bacteria. The bacteria enter the plant through wounds. They can also enter through natural openings, such as those in the leaves.

8.1 Give the name of the tiny 'natural openings' found in leaves.

....

[1]

8.2 The bacteria cannot pass through cell walls. Cell walls are a type of **physical defence** in plants. Give **one** other example of a **physical defence** in plants.

....

[1]

Another bacterial plant disease causes lumps to grow on a plant's stem or roots. The lumps grow due to the bacteria changing the plant's natural production of auxin.

8.3 During normal growth, active transport is needed to move auxin from one cell to a second cell. What does this tell you about the concentration of auxin in the second cell?

....

[1]

8.4 Describe how an uneven distribution of auxin within a plant shoot affects its growth.

....

....

[1]

8.5 The scientist took samples of the bacteria from several plants and grew them on Petri dishes. **Figure 6** shows one of these Petri dishes.

What is the area of the bacterial colony labelled **X** in **Figure 6**? Use the equation: area = πr^2. Give your answer in mm^2.

Figure 6

.... mm^2

[2]

[Total 6 marks]

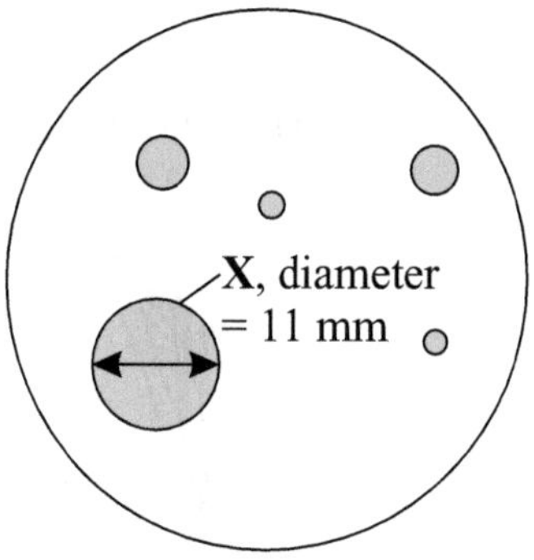

9 The life cycle of the protist that causes malaria is shown in **Figure 7**. Grade 4-5

9.1 Suggest **one** way of stopping the transfer of protists from mosquitoes to humans at point **A**.

....

....

....

[1]

9.2 Name the type of cell division that is occurring at point **B**.

....

[1]

Figure 7

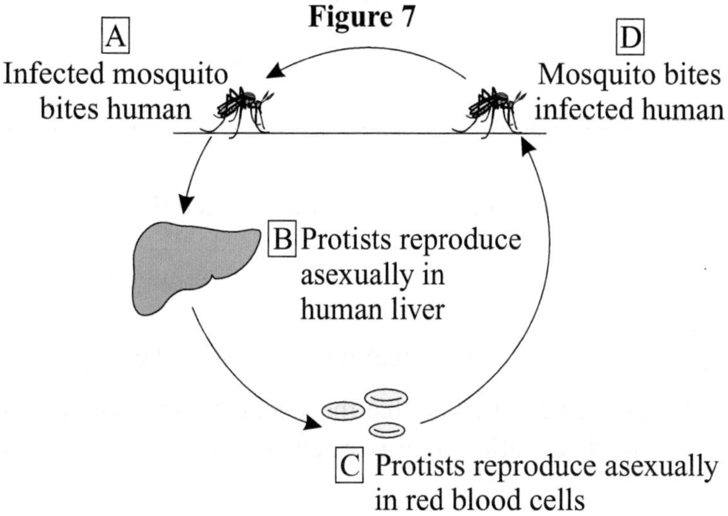

9.3 A symptom of malaria is feeling tired. Red blood cells are destroyed when a person is infected with malaria. This means there are fewer red blood cells to carry oxygen to body cells. Explain how this could cause someone to feel tired.

....

....

[1]

Exam Tip

Before you write your final answer in a calculation question, there are a couple of things to check. Make sure that you've shown your working, put the right numbers into your calculator and put the answer in the right units. You've got this.

9.4* The conditions inside the human body are favourable to the malaria protist.
Explain the advantages to the malaria protist of reproducing asexually in humans.

....

....

....

....

....

....

[4]

[Total 7 marks]

10 **Figure 8** shows an example of a grassland food chain. Grade 4-5

Figure 8

10.1 Grasses are the producer in this food chain.
What is meant by the term producer?

....

....

[1]

10.2 Give **one** biotic factor that may reduce the amount of grass in this food chain.

....

[1]

A scientist is investigating the grassland ecosystem.

10.3 Describe a method that the scientist could use to investigate whether the distribution of grasses changes across the ecosystem.

....

....

....

[3]

10.4 The scientist says: "The grassland is a stable community."
What is meant by a stable community?

....

....

[2]

[Total 7 marks]

BAFQ42